Net-Zero Trio
Synchronising Technology, Business and Policy for Green Transition

This timely book provides a crucial financial perspective on the diverse strategies needed to mitigate and adapt to climate change. It offers valuable insights into how India's financial sector can lead global efforts in mobilizing capital for green projects, while effectively integrating climate risk into decision-making processes.

– **Mr Navneet Munot,** *MD and CEO, HDFC AMC*

If you want to understand the threats and the opportunities in India's battle against climate change, there's no better place to start than Labanya Prakash Jena and Prasad Ashok Thakur's new book. It's a feast of insight, bringing together the latest thinking on a world-shaping transformation that's gathering pace across technology and policy, business and finance.

Mr Nick Robins, *Professor in Practice – Sustainable Finance and Executive Director, Just Transition Finance Lab, London School of Economics and Political Science (LSE)*

The "Net-Zero Trio Synchronising Technology, Business and Policy" by Prasad Ashok Thakur and Labanya Prakash Jena is a comprehensive guide that navigates the complexities of the energy transition with clarity and insight. The authors' complementary backgrounds and easy writing style illuminate the interplay of different elements that will shape our energy landscape, making this book a valuable resource for anyone interested in the future of our planet.

– **Mr Sumant Sinha,** *CEO, Renew*

This book is a great source of ideas. It contains a very useful compendium of writings by the authors. The topics are likely to be especially useful for climate policymakers, regulators, and decision-makers in international institutions. This will help design better policies and financial mechanisms to drive the adoption of low-carbon technologies and a sustainable, net-zero future.

It is a great book – for all interested in renewables. It talks of policy resources, financial mechanisms – and, most importantly, decision-making. A valuable resource for all of us to make the Earth healthy and liveable.

– **Dr Ajay Mathur,** *Director General, International Solar Alliance*

"Net-Zero Trio Synchronising Technology, Business and Policy for Green Transition" is a visionary blueprint charting India's pivotal journey towards a sustainable, low-carbon future. This definitive piece delves into the intricate interplay of technology, policy, business, and finance—crucial pillars that must seamlessly align for India to meet its ambitious climate goals. It offers an in-depth exploration of India's renewable energy landscape, pioneering solutions; while addressing the pressing challenges of financing cross-sectoral decarbonization. The book's sharp analysis of regulatory frameworks, underscores the necessity of a cohesive, forward-looking strategy to finance the green transition.

"Net-Zero Trio Synchronising Technology, Business and Policy for Green Transition" is an indispensable guide to navigating the challenges and seizing the opportunities that lie ahead in building a sustainable, resilient future for India. This book is an invaluable resource for understanding how sustainable growth can be achieved without compromising our planet's future.

– **Sh Amitabh Kant,** *India's G20 Sherpa, Government of India*

This book is a great source of ideas. It contains a very useful compendium of writings by the authors. The topics are likely to be especially useful for climate policymakers, regulators, and decision-makers in international institutions. This will help design better policies and financial mechanisms to drive the adoption of low-carbon technologies and a sustainable, net-zero future.

– **Mr Dipak Dasgupta,** *Distinguished Fellow TERI and IPCC Core Author*

Net-Zero Trio
Synchronising Technology, Business and Policy for Green Transition

Labanya Prakash Jena, CFA
Prasad Ashok Thakur

B L O O M S B U R Y
NEW DELHI • LONDON • OXFORD • NEW YORK • SYDNEY

BLOOMSBURY INDIA
Bloomsbury Publishing India Pvt. Ltd
Second Floor, LSC Building No. 4, DDA Complex,
Pocket C – 6 & 7, Vasant Kunj,
New Delhi 110070

BLOOMSBURY, BLOOMSBURY PRIME and the Diana logo are
trademarks of Bloomsbury Publishing Plc

First published in India 2024
This edition published in 2024

ISBN: 978-93-61316-38-8
2 4 6 8 10 9 7 5 3 1

Typeset by GRS Graphics, Delhi
Printed and bound in India by Replika Press Pvt. Ltd.

To find out more about our authors and books, visit
www.bloomsbury.com and sign up for our newsletters

Contents

Foreword

In the face of escalating climate change, the transition to green energy is not just a choice but an imperative. Our current dependence on carbon-intensive energy sources, products, and processes has caused a significant and adverse ecological impact that is worsening by the day. However, the ability to harness clean energy sources, development of circular economy models, and industrial process improvements – offer a beacon of hope. Such solutions promise not only to mitigate environmental impacts but also to foster economic growth, energy security, and social equity.

As per the International Energy Agency, the world now invests almost twice as much in clean energy (USD 2000+ billion) as compared to investments in fossil fuels (USD 1100+ billion) in the year 2023. China, the United States, and the European Union presently dominate the clean energy investment landscape. One of the primary reasons for this trend is the ability of clean energy generation technologies (especially wind and solar) to yield 2.5 times more energy output per dollar invested as compared to a decade ago. However, major imbalances in investment flows are observed, and Emerging Market Developing Economies outside China account for less than 20% of global clean energy spending. Thus, there is an urgent need to ensure technology cooperation, cross-border flow of green finance, and global policy alignment to ensure equitable development opportunities for all countries.

Here, international institutions have an important role to play in making available concessional finance for supporting climate adaptation and mitigation actions, especially for low- and middle-income nations. This is because such agencies have capital at their disposal and can raise additional finance from international markets at favourable conditions. At the grassroots level, they can provide technical and project management assistance, share global best practices, and conduct training/ human capability development programs. Additionally, such an approach can ensure the financial viability of trade and improve the resilience of clean energy supply chains. This book, "Net Zero Trio: Synchronizing Technology, Business, and Policy for Green Transition," offers a comprehensive exploration of the novel green technologies, innovative business models, and policy recommendations essential for achieving national and global Net-Zero targets.

The pages that follow provide innovative approaches for this transition. Each chapter typically starts with a lucid technical explanation of some of the most promising climate innovations that are observed globally. This is followed by discussions on business models to make this solution financially viable, both for the industry as well as the end consumer. This is followed by policy recommendations for its democratization and large scale adoption for achieving tangible impact. By integrating real-world case studies and expert insights, this book illuminates the path forward.

A rapid shift to a sustainable energy future at a global scale is a monumental task. Due to the diversity and complexity of the state of development in different parts of the globe, mobilizing concerted and decisive action is an art. Much like an orchestra. This book tries to role-play a 'conductor' that is attempting to synchronize 'the trio' of technology, business acumen, and policy to convert the dissonance in climate action into harmony.

I compliment the authors for their insightful compilation of articles. I am sure that these will be useful for all stakeholders and will help initiate debate and discussions on practical ways forward not only in India and the Global South, but for the entire world.

Prof. Amit Garg
Public Systems Group
National Investment & Infrastructure Fund (NIIF)
Chair in Environment, Social & Corporate Governance (ESG)
Indian Institute of Management Ahmedabad

Foreword

We stand at a pivotal moment in the journey of global economic and social progress. The 20th century delivered the most significant advance in human development, but the 21st century has posed significant challenges to this unprecedented path of improvement, the most pressing being climate change. Our pursuit of shared prosperity and well-being cannot continue unless we confront the climate crisis head-on. No nation or sector is exempt, compelling us to rethink the way the global economy is run. However, by effectively addressing these challenges, we have the potential to usher in an era of unparalleled economic opportunity and equality.

Therefore, the need for innovative business models, robust policy frameworks, favourable regulations, and substantial financial commitments has never been more critical. The book, "***Net-Zero Trio Synchronising Technology, Business and Policy for Green Transition***", with its global perspective and a particular focus on India, arrives at a crucial moment in this journey.

India—one of the world's most populous and rapidly developing nations—occupies a unique position in the global fight against climate change. The country's ambitious climate targets, coupled with its diverse economic landscape, present both challenges and opportunities. India's pathway to a net-zero future will require an integrated approach that combines technological innovation, financial acumen, supportive policy frameworks, and cooperation of international institutions. This book provides an in-depth exploration of these essential components, offering valuable insights into how India, and indeed the world, can navigate this complex transition.

Net-Zero Trio Synchronising Technology, Business and Policy for Green Transition provides a logical structure and pragmatic analysis of the components required for economic transition at speed and scale. The book explores the critical role that business innovations play in driving this transformation, the ecosystem required to support those innovations, and the central role of finance, both for funding the green transition and for finance itself to be sustainable. Importantly, the book also incorporates the role of international institutions, as global cooperation is essential for addressing a challenge as vast and complex as climate change.

This book is a call to action for all stakeholders—policymakers, business leaders, financiers, and international institutions—to come together and work towards a greener future. It challenges us to think creatively and collaboratively about the pathways to a net-zero world, emphasizing that the transition to a low-carbon economy is not just a technological or financial challenge but a comprehensive societal endeavour that can benefit all segments of society

As we stand on the brink of a new era in sustainable development, this book offers both the inspiration and the roadmap needed to guide us on our journey.

Dr Barbara Buchner
Global Managing Director
Climate Policy Initiative

Acknowledgements

The journey of writing this book has been both an enlightening and humbling experience. It has brought together a diverse group of minds, each contributing their unique perspectives and expertise to create a comprehensive resource on a subject of significant importance. This book is the result of collective efforts, and it is with deep gratitude that we acknowledge the contributions of all those who have made this work possible.

First and foremost, we would like to extend our heartfelt thanks to the contributors of this book: Gireesh Shrimali, Dhruba Purkayastha, Saurabh Trivedi, Jagjeet Sareen, Alexander Hogeveen Rutter, Vaibhav Chaudhary, Chinmaya Behera, Jolly Sinha, Vaibhav Pratap Singh, Shreyansh Jain, Rajashree Padmanabhi, Riya Saxena, Prof. Vikram Vishal, Meera Siva and Avinash Das. Your dedication, deep insights, and commitment to the subject matter have been instrumental in shaping the content of this book. Each chapter reflects your expertise and passion, and it is our hope that readers will benefit greatly from the knowledge you have shared. Your willingness to collaborate and engage in thoughtful discussions has enriched the quality of this book, and for that, we are immensely grateful.

We are also deeply appreciative of the distinguished individuals who have written the forewords for this book, Dr Amit Garg and Dr Barbara Buchner. Your words set the stage for the themes and ideas explored within these pages, providing readers with a compelling introduction to the topics at hand. We are honored to have your contributions at the forefront of this book. We also express our gratitude towards Mr Amitabh Kant, Dr Ajay Mathur, Mr Sumant Sinha, Mr Dipak Dasgupta, Mr Navneet Munot, and Mr Nick Robins for supporting our book.

We would also like to express our gratitude to the publishers—Observer Research Foundation (ORF), World Economic Forum (WEF), The Economic Times EnergyWorld, The Economic Times BFSI, Hindu Business Line, The Financial Express, Institute for Energy Economics and Financial Analysis (IEEFA), GITEX Impact, Carbon Copy, CFA Society India, Illuminem, Gateway House—who have played a crucial role in bringing this book to fruition.

A project of this magnitude is rarely accomplished without the encouragement and support of loved ones. We owe a profound debt of gratitude to our family members, whose unwavering support has been the cornerstone of our endeavors. To our parents, your guidance and encouragement have been a source of strength throughout this journey (Labanya Jena - Late Narayan Jena & Late Baijayanti Jena; Prasad Thakur - Mrs. Sandhya Jagtap & Mr. Ashok Jagtap). To our wives, your patience, understanding, and belief in the importance of this work have sustained us during the long hours of research and writing (Mrs. Mamata Jena; Mrs. Trupti Thakur). To our sisters (Namita & Mamata; Pradnya, Rucha & Kadambini), your love and support have provided us with the confidence to pursue our goals. To our sons (Pratyush and Prayas; Krishiv), your curiosity and enthusiasm have been a constant reminder of why we undertook this project. Without the backing of our family, this book would not have been possible, and we are eternally thankful for your influence in our lives.

We extend our thanks to all the readers and scholars who have and will engage with our writings, including this book. It is our hope that the knowledge, perspectives, and ideas shared within these pages will inspire further discussion, research, and action. The journey of knowledge is continuous, and we are honoured to contribute to this ongoing dialogue.

In conclusion, this book is a testament to the power of collaboration, the support of loved ones, and the commitment to advancing knowledge. We are deeply appreciative of everyone who has played a part in this journey, and we hope that this work will make a meaningful contribution to the field and beyond.

Introduction

Climate change accelerated by anthropogenic causes has far-reaching consequences. Rising temperatures pose a significant threat to not only humans but also the entire spectrum of global biodiversity. Additionally, the abrupt onslaught of heat/cold waves, coupled with shifts in precipitation patterns and increased frequency of natural calamities, has adversely impacted the fundamental developmental/evolutionary markers of flora and fauna, thus overturning the global food value chain.

Climate change is adversely affecting all countries, but South Asian countries, including India, are most vulnerable to climate change risks (HSBC, 2018). Further, South Asian countries are not only exposed to climate change risks but are also least prepared to mitigate climate change risks or adapt to climate change. ADB estimates suggest that climate impacts could reduce its annual gross domestic product by an average of 1.8 per cent by 2050, rising to 8.8 per cent by 2100 (ADB, 2014). The high density of economic activity and population, high dependence on monsoon for agriculture and home to 2/3 of the world's poor make India one of the most vulnerable countries to climate change risk. The physical impact of climate change, such as an increase in average temperature, water availability and extreme weather events are likely to affect India more severely than many other countries.

Moreover, India is more sensitive to extreme weather events such as drought, floods and extreme temperatures. The World Bank projects that climate change can reduce India's GDP by nearly 3 per cent and adversely affect the living standard of almost half of India's population (Mani et al., 2018). The estimated economic losses due to extreme weather events were USD$45 billion over 2008–17 vs. USD$20 billion over 1988–2007. India's Economic Survey 2017–18 (MoF, 2018) suggests that farmers' income could drop by 15 per cent to 18 per cent on average due to climate; the drop in income could increase up to 25 per cent in the unirrigated area. The fall in income translates into a drop in farmer's income by more than Rs 3,600 per year, which is more than 50 per cent of the Government's PM-KISAN scheme for farmers.

The key causes of climate change are increased concentrations of Greenhouse Gases (GHG) such as carbon dioxide (CO_2), methane (CH_4), Nitrous oxide (N_2O), etc. Power industry, industrial processes, transport and fuel exploitation are by far the largest drivers of GHG emissions globally. These emissions come primarily from burning fossil fuels.

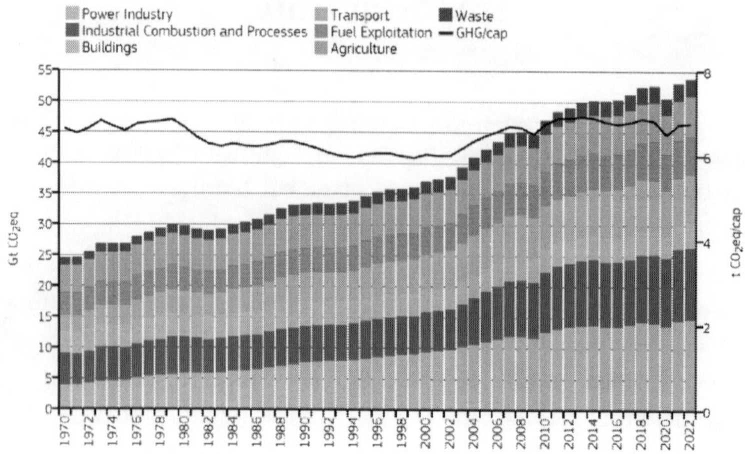

Figure 1: Global GHG Emissions by Sector (left axis, bars) and Per capita (right axis, black line), 1970–2022 (in Gt CO2eq)

Source: GHG emissions of all world countries, Publications Office of the European Union, Luxembourg, 2023, doi:10.2760/953332, JRC134504

Global Commitment

United Nations's Intergovernmental Panel on Climate Change (IPCC) emphasised the far-reaching adverse impacts of climate change, indicating a threshold of well within 2°C for rising global temperatures by the end of this century. This was significant and paved the way for the landmark UN Climate Change Conference (COP21) of 2015, underlining the goal of limiting rising global temperatures to 1.5°C above pre-industrial levels. The conference witnessed the institutionalising of the 'Paris Agreement'—the first multilateral climate change agreement that had a legal binding and was adopted by 196 countries globally. Implementation of the agreement entails parties must transform economically and socially, being supported by five-year plans that indicate a set of strategies that countries draw up to fight the adverse effects of climate change, by following adaptation and mitigation plans.

The countries have been submitting their climate action plans from 2020, also known as the nationally determined contributions (NDCs). While the Paris Agreement provides a base for the financial and technological support that is needed by the countries to further their climate action efforts, it reiterates the responsibility of the developed countries for the necessary capacity-building measures, technological transfer and financial aid that the developing economies need. The United Nations Framework Convention on Climate Change (UNFCCC) reports notable efforts from countries to reduce the GHGs and the steady rise of decarbonisation efforts and net-zero solutions. Starting 2024, all parties to the Paris Agreement will report their climate action progress along with the financial aid received through the enhanced transparency framework (ETF), feeding into the Global Stocktake, which will collectively evaluate the progress on climate action at a global level, bring out the gaps and help foster international cooperation as well as address the issues related to 'loss and damage'.

India's Commitment

The sheer size of India's population and economy and the potential for strong economic growth for the next two decades can make India the world's second-largest emitter after China by 2030. In November 2021, at the United Nations Climate Change Conference (COP26), India raised the bar for its climate commitments. It announced plans to reduce the carbon intensity of its economy by 45 per cent from 2005 levels by 2030 and achieve the target of net-zero by 2070. India further committed to reducing its total projected carbon emissions by one billion tonnes from 2021 to 2030, meeting 50 per cent of its energy requirements from renewable energy by 2030 and increasing its non-fossil energy capacity to reach 500 GW by 2030.

The strategic priorities have been stated through the Government of India's (GoI) formal framework, 'India's Long-term Low Carbon Development Strategy'. To achieve the targets set by India as part of the Paris Agreement and to transition to a low-carbon economy, it needs to deploy a wide range of technologies across energy-producing and consuming sectors, transportation, industrial processes, agriculture and other activities that emit GHG. In addition, India would also need to develop new solutions that can enhance the capacity and efficiency of carbon sinks to additionally sequester atmospheric carbon.

Sector	*Technologies*
Electricity Generation	Renewable electricity generation (wind, solar, hydro), battery storage, green hydrogen
Building	Energy efficiency, usage of less-carbon-intensive materials, recycling of construction materials
Transportation	Electrification, battery storage, green hydrogen, biofuels, ammonia, synfuels
Industrial	Electrification, green hydrogen, carbon capture and sequestration (CCS), bio-energy and recycling

India has made significant progress in several areas, such as renewables, energy efficiency, EVs and hydrogen. Despite the progress made, major challenges remain and rapid decarbonisation will be difficult to achieve. For instance, India's solar and wind capacity would need to increase from 151 GW in 2021 to 500 GW in 2030. This would require an acceleration in the annual build of ~40 GW from the current 10 GW a year. In addition, the transportation sector would have to be electrified rapidly, electrification of the industrial sector needs to be accelerated, commercialisation of green hydrogen and tremendous improvement in energy efficiency. All these require a significant drop in battery prices, setting up of nationwide charging infrastructure, green hydrogen cost (primarily cost of electrolysers) and implementation of effective carbon pricing to incentivise industries to use less-carbon-intensive plants and processes. To accelerate the transition, India needs to resolve supply-side bottlenecks, accelerate market reforms and storage buildout for the integration of renewables and grid reliability.

However, this ambitious target needs enormous capital to deploy these low-carbon technologies. Estimates by NITI Aayog (National Institution for Transforming India) indicate moderate low-carbon development would cost around USD 834 billion by 2030 at 2011 prices. According to the Council of Energy, Environment and Water (CEEW), India needs to mobilise $537 billion over 2020–30 (approx. $54 billion per annum) of capital for clean power, mobility and hydrogen. According to UBS, India requires an investment of $525 billion over 2022–30 towards installations (renewables, stationary batteries and electrolysers) and procurement (Electric vehicle batteries). However, capital flows into climate action are significantly lower than the requirements. Climate Policy Initiative (CPI's) India's Green Finance report suggests that capital mobilisation for the green sector (including adaptation) was USD 44 billion per annum over 2019–20, approximately a fourth of India's needs. ***According to CEEW, the investment gap could be USD 204 billion over 2020–30 if necessary policy and regulatory interventions still need to be put in place.***

Financing Options for India's Net-zero

Domestic household savings will play an important role in domestic investments and economic growth in India, including financing NDC plans. The share of household saving in total savings in India is about 58 per cent, followed by savings from non-financial corporations (32 per cent) and financial corporations (9 per cent). Approximately 58 per cent of household savings are preferably invested in physical assets not channelised into the economy. A large portion of these savings can also be channelised to climate action through financial intermediaries such as banks, pension funds, mutual funds and insurance.

Private financiers, including banks (managing approx. $4 trillion), institutional investors and specialised financial institutions, spread their investments across asset classes, geographies and sectors. They also use various financial instruments, such as loans, equity, bonds and structured finance, that allow them to participate in multiple economic activities. They invest directly in businesses (through loans and private equity) and indirectly (through stocks and bonds).

The sheer magnitude of financial assets under management controlled by commercial banks and institutional investors (pension funds, insurance companies and mutual funds) makes them an important source of financing for renewable energy. Given the availability of capital, the question now is how to attract and reorient private capital to the renewable energy sector. Although a significant amount of private capital is flowing to green sectors, the quantum of private capital flows is significantly less than the requirement. The major sources of capital to finance climate mitigation are likely to be banks, pension funds, insurance companies, mutual funds and Foreign Direct Investments (FDIs).

Challenges to Net-zero Financing

There are several challenges to accelerating private financing to economic activities; one of the key challenges is the heterogeneous characteristics of private financers (Kim and Park, 2016; Polzin, 2017). Hence, there is a need to match the characteristics of investees/economic activities with the investment objectives of different private financers. The common financial needs of most of the business models are upfront capital, long-term capital and high-risk capital for research and development (R&D).

There are several challenges to India's transition to low-carbon economic development. Some are idiosyncratic to the green sectors, while others are more standard. The idiosyncratic barriers are an absence of a clear definition of green finance, oversight in internalising the cost of environmental externalities in the financing, information asymmetry and lack of historical performance record to assess financing risks. The generic barriers include startup phase technologies, unproven business models, long-term financing needs and the dearth of appropriate financial instruments.

Policy and Regulatory Interventions Across the System

Strong financial support and timely policy interventions from India's government can play a crucial role in financing the transition and incentivising private sector participation to scale up investments in green sectors. There are many initiatives that have been taken by many countries, including India, to address those barriers, such as taxing carbon-emitting sectors, subsidising green economic activities and bending regulations favouring green economic activities. These initiatives have brought success in the renewable energy sector in India, which reflected an upsurge in renewable investments in India over the past few years. A major policy push by the Government of India along with drop in technology prices, catalysed investments in renewable energy. However, there has been a limited investment made in other green economic activities; while this is an excellent way to divert capital flows into a sector, a similar level of policy and regulatory measures are needed to divert capital flows to other green economic activities directed towards achieving India's sustainable development goals.

Need to Develop Innovative Financial Mechanisms and Instruments

The safety investment principle does not allow institutional investors, including pension funds and insurance companies in low-carbon technologies. There is a high perceived and actual risk associated with these technologies due to limited track record and understanding of climate project dynamics, policy and regulatory uncertainties, technology risk, etc. The structural and institutional constraints are not allowing large investors to deploy capital in low-carbon technologies. For example, pension funds and insurance companies are discouraged from investing in low-rated securities. So, risks associated with low-carbon technologies need to be brought down to same level as of conventional businesses, which can attract these low risk-seeking capital. Hence, there is a need to create novel financial mechanisms and instruments which can help them to access funds from these classes of investors.

Role of Development Financial Institutions (DFIs) and Multilateral Development Banks (MDBs)

DFIs and MDBs provide critical capital, manage risks, share knowledge and develop institutional capacity and partnerships for development projects in target countries. DFIs include domestic government-backed development banks, Multilateral Development Banks (MDBs) and Development Financial

Institutions (DFIs). They are set up to accelerate funding for development activities (Dickinson, 2008), including low-carbon economic activities. Unlike private investors, DFIs and MDBs can finance risky projects and technologies, real and/or perceived, sending a positive signal about the projects or technologies to the market. Sometimes, they can also participate as risky investors in the projects, which reduces the riskiness of the projects. The risk-taking and risk-reductive investment approach of DFIs and MDBs can be useful for low-carbon technologies and projects at different stages of riskiness till fully accepted by commercial financers. MDBs and DFIs have a mandate to invest in riskier and more impactful sectors and countries, so they need to take risks and be open to investing through various financial instruments to create financial and developmental additionality.

ADVANCING NET-ZERO TECHNOLOGIES: BUSINESS INNOVATIONS AND POLICY FRAMEWORK

Net-Zero: India's Opportunity to Play its Ace[1]

As per the Emissions Gap Report 2021 of the UNEP, the world has so far failed to embark on a trajectory towards limiting global warming to 1.5°C. While developed countries have financial resources and technology access, the least developed countries (LDCs) and small island developing countries (SIDs) await the necessary support as per Article 10 of the Paris Agreement. As the commitments from developed countries to these vulnerable countries have not been followed-up by adequate actions, India can rise to the occasion by positioning itself as a climate leader through principled and pragmatic ventures. India has already delivered on its Paris Agreement commitments in 'letter and spirit'. It has now committed to an ambitious plan to cut down the carbon intensity of its economy by more than 45 per cent by 2030 and achieve net-zero by 2070. This announcement has taken a pole position amongst the large developing economies in shaping global conversations around the topic of climate equity. These declarations have resonated well with the nations of the Global North and South. India can now leverage its intellectual and technological prowess coupled with its soft power to achieve its rightful stature in the global order. It can begin by supporting the LDCs and SIDs through outcome-based interventions to realise the elusive 'Global Net-Zero'.

Clarity in Articulation of National Strategies

Overcoming its own constraints, India can commit focused resources towards understanding the needs of LDC and SIDs on climate action. It can share learnings from its people-centric developmental models, indigenous technologies, programme management expertise and inclusive policies while being respectful towards the priorities of individual countries. Such actions can liberate LDCs and SIDs from heavy expectations of financial reciprocity. To begin with, India can support them in preparing for the global stocktake of the Paris Agreement (GST) 2023 through local capacity building. Such support can trickle in through various bilateral and multilateral initiatives. It

[1] The article was written by Labanya Prakash Jena and Prasad Ashok Thakur and was first published by the Observer Research Foundation. https://www.orfonline.org/expert-speak/net-zero-indias-opportunity-to-play-its-ace

is important to note that the outcome of this GST is expected to influence the drafting of new NDCs for the post-2023 phase. India can help synchronise global climate actions across geographies to help them become more relevant, impactful and sustainable.

Purposeful actions in a few sectors can yield disproportionately large favourable outcomes. Renewed thrust on promoting renewable energy, electric mobility, sustainable built-environment and smart-agriculture can result in rapid, inclusive and sustainable benefits. Although each sector has a unique structure and distinct growth-dynamics, a holistic value-chain approach on climate action that includes multilateral agencies, local/state/union governments, private sector, civil society and academia can be transformational. Intensifying sector-focused peer-to-peer knowledge-sharing avenues at each stratum of these value-chains can unlock substantial opportunities for all stakeholders. The participation of diverse countries in India-led initiatives like International Solar Alliance, Centre for Disaster Resilient Infrastructure, Centre for Space Science and Technology Education for Asia and the Pacific (CSSTE-AP), Startup India International Summit, etc., have reinforced the utility of such initiatives.

Invoking 'Commercial Diplomacy'

Indian business associations such as Confederation of Indian Industry (CII), FICCI, ASSOCHAM, NASSCOM can contribute substantially towards the global 'circular economy' discourse. They can become leading ambassadors for propagating India's commercial diplomacy on climate action. They can facilitate the exchange of climate-smart practices with peers in LDCs and SIDs. Creating country-specific systems for capturing market intelligence, catalysing growth of innovative micro, small and medium enterprises and establishing skills training through CSR funds are some measures that can create 'local green jobs'. These measures will improve the macroeconomic stability in such countries and can facilitate their integration into the global economy. The government's diplomatic efforts should complement corporates' actions in this direction.

Green Capital: Conduit for Collaboration

From a supply perspective, developed countries' current commitment to climate finance is not commensurate with their GHG emissions. Their actual disbursements are far lesser than their declared commitments. Moreover, they tend to label private finance extended at market rates as their financial support for climate action. Thus, focused and consistent capital mobilisation for green initiatives has become a perpetual challenge for most LDCs and SIDs facing constraints like low per-capita income, volatile economy, lack of fiscal space and low savings rate. It is worth noting that these countries have also committed to ambitious decarbonisation targets to capitulate to global pressures. As a principled player on the world stage, India can help them articulate such inconsistencies on global forums with assertiveness. This may lead to increased commitments and release of 'real' climate finances, especially for the post-2023 phase.

The inability of LDCs and SIDs to fully leverage international public climate finance mechanisms, e.g., Green Climate Fund (GCF), is worrisome. Moreover, private capital providers are reluctant to invest in such economies due to a lack of bankable projects and favourable eco-systems for 'green-sectors'. Bridging such viability gaps is critical for the world. India can leverage its innovation and expertise in the financial sector to benefit such countries. It can also support them with capacity and institution building, best practices in financial governance and infusion of climate action in economic policies. India's intricate support to LDCs and SIDs in creating project design, planning, execution and controlling can improve the bankability of large-scale 'green-programmes', thus opening doors for the flow of finance. They are emeralds studded on the surface of our blue marble. Through its actions and demeanour, India can summon the world on a path of higher purpose: To soar above a constricted view of country-specific interests and realise that each of us can serve our interests better by working together as equals in reinvigorating multilateralism to shape our common future.

Renewable Energy Generation

Accelerating renewable energy generation will be the key to global ambition to arrest global warming as the energy sector contributes ~70 per cent of GHG emissions. It is no different in India. The power (electricity generation) sector, contributing ~34 per cent of GHG emissions, is the central focus of the government. In 2011–22, fossil fuel (coal and natural gas) contributed to 74 per cent of electricity generation in India, followed by renewable energy (22.2 per cent) and nuclear energy (3.15 per cent).[1] In addition, the decarbonisation of other energy-consuming sectors also needs to be electrified substantially, which needs further demand for electricity generation. India is striving to electrify its transportation and industrial sectors so that it can source electricity from non-renewable energy instead of fossil fuels.

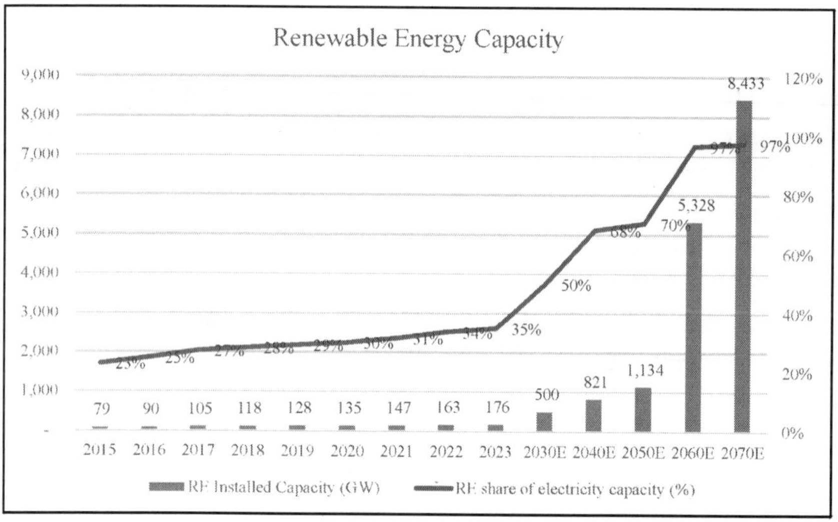

Source: Historical (IRENA), 2030 (India's NDC Target), Forecast (CEEW)

The government has a target to increase electricity from renewable energy sources by adding 330 GW of renewable energy capacity over 2022–30. A McKinsey study suggests that India needs to add 134 GW capacity per annum by 2050 to reach net-zero compared to only 18.5 GW in 2023. However, the slow adoption of renewable energy capacity addition does not

[1] https://www.orfonline.org/expert-speak/fuel-mix-in-power-generation-in-india-present-and-future/

give confidence that India can achieve its near-term target of cumulative 500 GW by 2030 from 170 GW in 2023, which needs an annual capacity addition of 50 GW compared to a 2023 capacity addition of 18.5 GW in 2023. More than two times capacity addition each year needs urgent measures—starting from easy land acquisition to honouring contractual commitments.

The challenges are a combination of financing, policy and regulatory, technology and operational as outlined below.

Financing Challenges	Operational and Technical Challenges	Policy and Regulatory Challenges
• DISCOM's financial health • Foreign currency risk • Refinancing risk • High-cost of energy storage • Over reliance on banks and NBFC for debt financing needs	• Bottleneck in Solar Photovoltaic (PV) Supply Chain • Land acqusition issues • Lack of grid connectivity • Inter-state transmission	• Achieving Renewable Energy Purchase Obligations (RPOs) • Lack of support from DISCOMs • No updation of state energy policy • Inter-State Transmission System (ISTS) Market Challenges

Source: Multiple

Developing Operational and Technical Capacity

Attracting foreign solar PV manufacturers, developing solar PV manufacturing capacity and increasing R&D investment in manufacturing can help India develop a solar Photovoltaic (PV) supply chain that is ready to meet the demand of India's capacity requirements. Besides, the development of energy storage capabilities at local and regional levels can address intermittency issues of renewable energy. Heavy investment on grid infrastructure for renewable energy evacuation and transmission is necessary to supply RE across the country without infrastructure challenges.

Policy and Regulatory Supports and Interventions

The continuation of exemption in ISTS charges, the meaningful penalties for RPO annual energy shortfall, nudging states to reform DISCOMs and improving technical capacity can bring policy and regulatory stability to the renewable energy ecosystem. Rooftop solar targets by each state, financial incentives to banks and NBFCs supporting the deployment of rooftop solar in the MSMEs and quick disbursal of loans for residential solar can accelerate rooftop solar adoption.

The existing policy and regulatory framework are designed for large regulated government-owned utilities working on administered dispatch and balancing services with limited interaction between different sectors, which supports the convergence of multiple sectors and thereby enables greater RE Integration. Development of technology-agnostic Ancillary and Real-Time Markets for the sale of balancing services, which foster the growth of low-cost innovative solutions like active demand response from services like space cooling. Regulatory planning for integration of a large number of EVs and delivery of appropriate price signals to drive charging behaviour that is favourable to grid requirements and does not aggravate balancing needs. Policy and market framework that gives space for the creation of innovative business models such as storage as service providers or aggregators for demand response from domestic consumers. Development of policy and regulatory structures that allow for the creation of financial contracts such as 'Tradable PPAs' or 'Financial Transmission Rights' which lead to greater commerce in the sector and improve efficiency.

Financial Interventions

The public sector can play an enabler's role by designing policies and programmes that create a conducive environment for investors in the sector. A vigorous business environment can move up the risk-return outline of a sector and consequently draw private investors' attention toward the sector. Moreover, the public sector can also invest (through budgetary support) in the renewables sector. One of the best usages of public capital is to mitigate the risks of investments by addressing the obstacles the private financers are facing. For example, guarantees such as credit enhancement support help private investors build the confidence necessary to attract more finance into the sector (WEF, 2013). Several governments and multinational financial institutions provide financial support to address early-stage project development issues. The green hydrogen and battery storage sector are not fully commercially viable yet, so the government must support them by providing grants/subsidies and concessional loans to accelerate the adoption of technologies.

Improved DISCOM's financial health through electricity distribution sector reform can decrease counterparty risk of the renewable energy sector; political willingness can make DISCOMs a financially sustainable entity that offers comfort in the electricity sector. The availability of long-term financing can decrease the refinancing risk of the sector; raising debt capital from long-term institutional investors can reduce refinancing risk. The use of financial instruments such as AIF, InVIT and securitisation, along with partial credit guarantee, can help the sector use these instruments to raise long-term debt capital from institutional investors. Foreign exchange risk is one the principal barriers to attracting foreign debt capital. Accessibility of long-term swaps at a reasonable price can reduce foreign exchange risk that accelerates foreign debt capital to the renewable energy sector. Multilateral development banks and the government can use FX hedging instruments to reduce the hedging cost of foreign capital. Expensive energy storage is still a bottleneck to the rapid adoption of renewable energy. Smart use of public capital can scale up energy storage capacity (e.g., battery, green hydrogen, etc.), which can reduce the cost of energy storage quickly and accelerate the adoption of energy storage.

Solar Sector

Solar energy is abundant, being harnessed from sunlight and raw materials for electricity production from solar systems are readily available. While an increase in the scale of production, thanks to governments across the world, decreased production costs significantly, experience also improved the performance of solar energy systems over time. The lower manufacturing cost of solar energy made solar a competitive source of electricity compared to other sources of electricity, including fossil fuel (e.g., coal and natural gas). The levelised cost of electricity (LCOE) of solar decreased from $12 per kwH in 2012 to $6 per kWh, which propelled the massive addition of solar in India in the last decade. Solar capacity increased from a mere 5.7 GW (0.5 per cent of total electricity capacity) to 73.1 GW in 2023 (17.3 per cent of total electricity capacity). Solar is expected to continue to be a key source of clean and overall source of electricity. Hence, it is the most critical technology to decarbonise the energy system. Over 2024–30, solar capacity addition is expected to be 200 GW to meet India's NDC target and will be key to India's net-zero ambition.

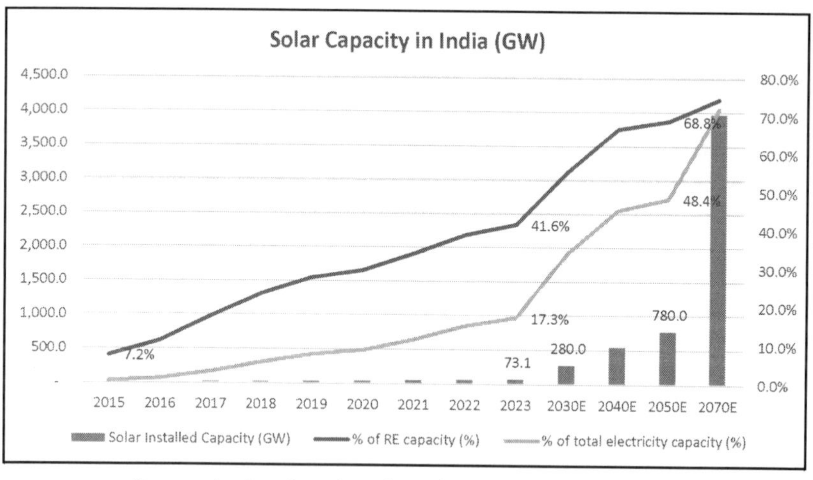

Source: Authors' analysis based on IRENA and CEEW

Government Policy Propelled the Adoption of the Solar Sector

The solar sector enjoyed all the policy benefits targeted to the renewable energy sector. Besides, the Government of India has introduced several measures to propel the adoption of solar as a primary source of electricity, including setting up of Solar Energy Corporation of India (SECI), solar parks, generation-based incentives (GBI), viability gap funding (VGF), taxation funding benefits and solar subsidy scheme.

SECI's transparent and competitive tendering procedure accelerated the development of utility-scale solar parks. Another breakthrough intervention of SECI is creating a payment security mechanism (PSM) that addresses the counterparty risk, delay or default by DISCOMs to pay energy to solar energy developers, one of the most critical risks for investors and lenders in the renewable energy sector in India. Solar Park is one of the key initiatives by the government to reduce risks in the solar energy sector. Solar Park—a plug-and-play model—was able to attract large investors, particularly low-risk seeking investors, to the solar energy sector by reducing implementation and project risks. The Solar Park model addressed some of the major risks, such as land acquisition, power evacuation, water access and infrastructure development. Other schemes such as GBI, VGF, taxation benefits and subsidies made the solar sector attractive for investment. In recent years, the Government of India also has new policies such as making rooftop solar a priority sector lending (PSL) category, PM-Kusum Yojana (solar plus water for farmers and Pradhan Mantri Suryodaya Yojana (subsidy for installing rooftop solar by households) targeted for distributed solar.

Scaling up the Solar Sector: Challenges Galore

Despite a number of favourable policies, the solar sector target did not achieve the desired result. The Government of India had a target of reaching 100 GW of solar energy by March 2022 but could install only 62 GW by that time. While the utility-scale solar segment's capacity addition was close to the target (Actual 50 GW vs. a target of 60 GW), rooftop solar lagged far from the target (Actual 40 GW vs. 15 GW). Supply chain disruptions (availability of supply modules and delay), land acquisition, transmission and evacuation of renewable energy challenges, lack of storage, policy flip-flops and lack of long-term debt financing are the key bottlenecks to the overall solar sector in India, including the utility segment. There are additional challenges to the rooftop solar segment. Lack of access to finance at a reasonable rate, unreliable and unreasonable net metering policies, lack of support from DISCOMs and cumbersome process to access subsidies squeezed the adoption of the rooftop solar sector.

Vigorous Policies and Regulations Required to Scale up the Sector

To increase capacity addition from 10 GW per year to 40 GW per year needs vigorous policies and regulations to address several challenges. Lowering tariff and non-tariff barriers, although not removing, on solar equipment till India has developed an adequate manufacturing base and supply chain can address the availability of solar equipment at a competitive price in the short term. The public sector, Power Grid Corporation of India in particular, must invest in grid-infrastructure to evaluate and transmit solar from hinterland and challenging terrain. On the other hand, energy storage, initially battery and green hydrogen, thereafter, will be key to making solar as 24/7 source of electricity supply. The government can spearhead the development of solar plants across the country that can address land acquisition issues.

Rooftop Solar

Spreading of consumer awareness, particularly in Tier-3 cities and villages about the benefits of solar energy along with procedures to obtain government benefits and EPC developers can educate households and MSMEs to adopt rooftop solar. The central and state government with the support of local industry associations, banks, solar EPCs and panchayats, can undertake this exercise. Streamlining net-metering approvals by DISCOMs can simplify the process for consumers to integrate the system with the grid. Quick approval of the central and state subsidy scheme for rooftop solar systems can encourage consumers to opt for rooftop solar. MSMEs, particularly energy-intensive, benefit from rooftop solar systems as the cost of electricity from owned rooftop solar systems (INR 4-5 per kWH) is significantly less than grid-based electricity (INR 7-8 per kWh). The availability of financing at an affordable rate to MSMEs can support them with rooftop solar.

Battery

The intermittent nature of solar technology does not make it a primary and reliable source of energy. Energy storage combined with the solar system can make solar a stable and core energy supplier. However, the deployment of energy storage is limited in India. Battery as a medium of storage technology is reliable and commercially feasible in several segments of the energy sector.

Battery for energy storage needs substantial customer commitment before system deployment. Battery storage projects require a large upfront investment but make economic sense considering electricity bill savings and low operating costs over the life cycle of the battery. Financing is one of the reasons batteries as an electricity storage solution have not accelerated in these countries. It is limited to private equity players, corporates (mainly renewable energy players) and venture capital funds, which invest a small amount of capital for battery storage. However, the large-scale deployment of batteries requires the substantial capital deployment of large financers such as banks and institutional investors.

The limited performance record of battery economics and lack of a secondary market makes it harder for these financers to invest in battery technology and look for collateral-based financing. Besides, there are other unique barriers attached to financing battery. Those are the lack of long-term contracts, the need for electricity-generating companies and performance guarantees.

An exclusive financing facility blending private and public capital can address these challenges. The financing facility can raise patience high risky equity capital from the private sector, for example, private equity and the public sector, for example, government, DFIs (e.g., International Finance Corporation) and green financial institutions. The financial facility can also raise long-term debt capital from a combination of development financial institutions (DFIs) and commercial banks. In the capital structure of the facility, the commercial banks can hold senior positions compared to debt from DFIs. The availability of long-term capital can help battery operators (selling energy storage as a service), or renewable energy companies (using the battery as storage) deploy batteries.

Investment by public financers at the early stage can demonstrate the battery segment's financial performance as a technically reliable and commercially profitable proposition. This can assure the energy selling company to enter into a long-term contract with the battery operator or allocate its own capital for buying batteries for energy storage. The performance record can also reduce the perceived risk that can attract low-risk and long-term debt capital from commercial banks and institutional investors.

Solar PV Manufacturing

The solar PV manufacturing facility is highly capital intensive and also needs working capital as the manufacturer provides credit to customers. Here, access to finance and terms of financing plays a significant role in attracting large-scale investment for solar manufacturing. Besides, the manufacturer also needs to invest in research and development (R&D) to continuously improve the efficiency of the solar PV system. While large corporates can use their balance sheet capital to set up new manufacturing facilities or expand existing operations, medium size operators are struggling to raise capital, particularly debt capital, at a reasonable rate to meet the funding needs of solar manufacturing. A blending of grant and long-term debt capital at a reasonable rate and privately funded equity capital can address these challenges.

When the scale of operation of manufacturing reaches a critical mass, grants would no longer be required. The manufacturer also needs long-term debt capital at a reasonable rate. Since manufacturing has a long investment cycle, the mix of concessional debt capital and grants can increase return on equity, thereby attracting corporate or private equity investors even if higher risks are associated with solar PV manufacturing. The blending of commercial and concessional debt capital can reduce the cost of debt. The DFIs and green financing institutions can offer long-term debt at a lower rate and take a risky position in the capital structure compared to commercial debt financers. This kind of capital structure can give sufficient protection to private debt financers to offer debt capital for solar PV manufacturing. The blend of private and public debt can not only address the access to capital challenge but also meet the long-term low-cost debt funding needs of manufacturers. The low-cost funding offered by the Chinese Development Bank (CDB), backed by the Chinese Government's guarantee, to solar PV manufacturers, made the industry competitive and efficient.

At the same time, the solar sector also needs continuous investment in R&D to improve efficiency and reduce per unit cost of production. Till the corporates reach when the return on investment in solar manufacturing justifies its risk, they will not invest in R&D. The government can provide financing for R&D that can be blended with corporates' balance sheet capital to fund R&D expenses. Besides, the government capital can be blended with a corporation's balance sheet capital to acquire foreign technologies. Historically, the governments in industrial economies have supported corporates in their R&D efforts. Manufacturing solar creates public goods, although indirectly; this justifies public financing.

Wind Sector

The escalating global concern over environmental degradation has sparked a keen interest in renewable energy resources. Wind power stands out as the most commercially and operationally viable option among these. It is rapidly emerging as one of the largest contributors to the renewable energy sector. Wind, the movement of air across land and sea, results from uneven heating and cooling of the earth's surface and the planet's rotation. Differential heat absorption by land and water leads to warm air rising and cooler air replacing it, creating local winds. The earth's rotation influences the direction of airflow.

Understanding Technology

Wind turbines transform the kinetic energy of the wind into electricity through a rotor, gearbox and generator. When spun by the wind, the blades rotate a shaft to which they are connected. This rotating shaft can operate a pump or drive a generator to produce electricity. The majority of wind machines have blades affixed to a horizontal shaft. Through a series of gears, this shaft delivers power to a water pump or an electric generator, forming what is known as horizontal axis wind turbines. There are also vertical axis machines, such as the 'Darrieus' wind machine, which is equipped with two to four elongated, curved blades on a vertical shaft, resembling a colossal eggbeater. The energy output of a wind machine is contingent on the wind speed and the size of the blades. Generally, if the wind speed doubles, the power output increases eightfold. Larger blades can capture more wind, and if the diameter of the circle formed by the blades double, the power output quadruples.

Wind energy offers numerous benefits for power generation. The initial investment for wind farms is on par with traditional power plants, with costs ranging from 4.5 to 6.85 crore per MW, contingent on factors such as turbine type, technology, size and location. The construction phase is relatively brief, with minimal operational and maintenance costs. Another advantage is the absence of fuel costs, making it a cost-effective solution in the long run. The capacity can be expanded in a modular manner, providing flexibility in power generation. Moreover, wind energy is a green solution that doesn't contribute to environmental pollution, making it a sustainable and eco-friendly choice for power generation. This system does not negatively impact the global environment, underscoring its viability as a clean energy source.

India's Wind Energy Sector

India's economic growth and well-being hinge on clean, reliable, affordable power access alongside a robust manufacturing sector supporting this renewable energy push. The current phase of the wind energy sector highlights India's favourable chances to leverage domestic and international opportunities for wind market expansion.

India's wind energy sector has steadily advanced, spearheaded by its indigenous wind power industry. The wind industry's growth has fostered a robust ecosystem, project management capabilities and an annual domestic manufacturing capacity of approximately 12 GW. As of 30 April 2024, India holds the 4th position globally regarding wind installed capacity, with a total capacity of 46.16 GW and a pipeline of 31.17 GW. Furthermore, the wind power projects in the country have produced 203 million units on the above date. This consistent progress highlights the expansion of India's wind industry and underscores its potential to contribute to the country's renewable energy portfolio. The sector's achievements are a testament to the country's commitment to harnessing wind energy and its potential for future growth.

India's cumulative onshore wind energy capacity is projected to reach 65+ GW by 2027, 215 GW by 2040 and about 300 GW by 2050, per a CEEW report titled 'Investment Sizing India's 2070 Net-Zero Target'. A strategy paper from the Ministry of New and Renewable Energy (MNRE), Government of India, outlines a plan to award 37 GW of offshore wind tenders by 2030 in Gujarat and Tamil Nadu.

Existing robust project pipelines, RPO obligations, bid trajectory announcements and grid planning will propel India's wind energy sector. Besides, significant opportunities in the offshore wind market and the requirements from an emerging green hydrogen ecosystem will make wind the second most important lean energy source in India's power mix.

However, challenges such as right-of-way issues, streamlining policy, delays in budget allocation and financing restrictions may cause temporary roll-back or abandoning of some projects.

Challenges aplenty

India's 750 GW wind energy potential faces myriad challenges hindering sector growth, including right-of-way issues, streamlining policy, lack of adequate infrastructure, delays in budget allocation and financing restrictions.

One of the most significant challenges to realising this potential is the country's inadequate transmission infrastructure. Wind power's intermittency requires a robust network to transport electricity from wind farms to consumers, but India's current system cannot efficiently handle the large volumes of intermittently generated wind power. Insufficient capacity of power lines and substations hinders electricity transport, leading to grid congestion.

For optimum wind energy generation, wind energy farms need extensive land parcels as the positioning of the large turbines must be accurately calibrated and adequately spaced. This requirement poses challenges in densely populated countries like India.

Wind energy may also come along with a few cost challenges. The price and installation cost of state-of-the-art wind turbines are still considered expensive. Wind power can be pricier at certain locations than coal or natural gas, making it non-competitive.

As these dynamics play out, wind power's variable output results in fluctuations in electricity supply, thus bringing grid management to the fore. Here, the pace of data and monitoring systems commissioning is not as expected. The limited real-time information on wind power systems hampers effective decision-making in operations and maintenance.

Additionally, the physical structure of wind machines, including towers and turbine blades, is vulnerable to high winds and lightning damage, making maintenance challenging and costly. The noise produced by the rotating blades of wind machines can be a nuisance to those living nearby. Aesthetically, wind machines have been criticised, raising concerns about their impact on bird populations.

Technology Solutions

The challenge of intermittency of wind energy can be better managed if renewable energy generation projects include a combination of solar, wind, energy storage, electricity banking facilities, etc. This can also help reduce the cost of electricity obtained from such projects and support the evolving requirements of RTC (round-the-clock) power.

The introduction of digital twin technologies (DT) can generate and analyse real-time data about energy systems across the generation, transmission and consumption value chain. DT models can integrate and produce actionable recommendations on a giga-scale basis. Along with increased energy generation, this can help in setting up predictive maintenance protocols for wind energy systems. Based on insights gained through such objective and accurate data, training modules can be created to upskill the people resources of the country to seize the 'green jobs' created domestically and globally.

Policy Prescriptions

To facilitate grid integration of wind energy generated in renewable energy parks located at hitherto unconnected areas, key stakeholders in governments, the private sector and local communities must jointly arrive at a winning formula for solving land availability issues for 'right of way'(ROW) of greenfield transmission lines and associated substations.

The union government's 2023 guidelines for tariff-based bidding for grid-connected wind projects follow a two-part (techno-commercial) bidding process. Moreover, it also supports an e-reverse auction mechanism by the procurer/intermediate procurer at their discretion. The latter may put downward price pressures and significant tariff reductions in each successive round of tenders. This runs contrary to the purpose of the guidelines, which aim to curtail the volume-seeking tendencies of bidders who later surrender the awarded volume. Sufficient oversight must be introduced to ensure that challenges emanating from this are removed proactively.

Unlocking for commercial and industrial segments, green open access markets is critical. Post Green Open Access Rules, a few states like West Bengal, Karnataka and Punjab have updated their policies. However, hurdles like reliability charges and restrictive power banking provisions make green power costly. Governments need to work with DISCOMs to enable green electricity for the C&I segment economically, with regular progress monitoring.

Various states have proactively established a wind Renewable Purchase Obligation (RPO) to encourage the adoption of wind energy. While this initiative is commendable, it is essential to implement policy measures to ensure adherence. In cases of defaults or non-compliance, policymakers should consider implementing appropriate penalties. Regulatory commissions must prevent situations where other technology RPOs fulfil the wind RPO. Before allowing such substitutions, the commission should carefully evaluate the efforts made by DISCOMs to meet the wind RPO. Most importantly, the RPO trajectories established by states must align with the overall national targets, supported by coordinated RPO calculation methodologies between central and state governments.

The transportation of wind project machinery and equipment requires adequate surface transport infrastructure. Properly planned corridors during project implementation and equipment shipment would help reduce transportation and logistics time and costs, thereby lowering overall project costs for consumers. Creating adequate infrastructure could also support repowering existing units with new, higher-capacity turbines and larger blades.

The volatility in commodity prices used to manufacture wind turbines, such as steel, iron and copper, challenges the commercial feasibility of awarded wind projects. An increase in the prices of these commodities could spike capital expenditure. It could result in a depressing expected return on investment, making lenders and equity investors uneasy about investing in wind projects. Incorporating commodity prices in bidding guidelines and Power Purchase Agreement (PPA) documents can mitigate this risk for investors.

India's Emergence as an Export Hub for Supporting Global Wind Energy

India can align itself to become a major global export hub for wind energy infrastructure components. The country accounts for an estimated nacelle capacity of 11 GW/year. With optimistic scenarios projecting capacity additions of about 6 GW, spare capacity remains that can be strategically leveraged for both South Asian and global wind markets.

The global onshore wind installations are expected to grow significantly, increasing from about 70 GW in 2022 to 125+ GW by 2027. This surge in demand translates to a 50+ GW requirement for nacelle assembly. India can capitalise on this manufacturing opportunity and export nacelles, particularly to the USA and emerging wind regions in the Asia-Pacific, Africa and West Asia.

In addition to nacelles, there is potential in wind component manufacturing. Currently, companies rely on China to source critical components. It dominates the global supply chain, accounting for over 60 per cent of blades, generators and gearbox manufacturing. With its existing and upcoming manufacturing base, India can aim to contribute at least 25 per cent global capacity—up from the present levels of ~10 per cent share for these components. This positions India as a key player in the wind energy export ecosystem, driving growth and sustainability beyond its borders.

Currently, wind turbine prototypes are primarily developed and tested outside India. The central government can take steps to encourage domestic prototype development, testing and research and development (R&D). In addition, the central government can offer grants for R&D and innovation through universities, research institutions, public-private partnerships, preferential tax treatment and the development of necessary manpower by joining hands with local engineering colleges. All these measures could boost local investment in the wind manufacturing supply chain and support the expansion of wind manufacturing in India.

Floating Offshore Wind: A Potential Solution to Meet Global Decarbonisation Needs[1]

Floating offshore wind turbines are affixed on platforms that are firmly moored to the ocean bed and connected by dynamically suspended cables. As a technology, floating offshore wind (FOW) can be considered supplementary to fixed-seabed wind technology. It deploys fixtures and component configurations that are compatible with conventional systems, including power substations, undersea transmission networks and feed-in infrastructure of the existing grids. The deployment of FOW turbines in open seas involves conventional tugboats, buoys and anchors. These characteristics enable FOW to function in tandem with the existing electrical ecosystems and established component supply chains. The newly given access to deeper waters allows for cherry-picking of offshore wind farm site locations that offer the highest wind speeds while aiming for the lowest possible environmental and socio-economic impacts.

Huge Energy Generation Potential

Unlike other renewable energy sources, offshore wind power has a significant advantage in generating substantial amounts of electricity. The International Energy Agency (IEA) projects that the annual global potential for offshore wind power generation can be over 420,000 TWh, more than sixteen times the global power demand, with the year 2022 as a reference. In addition, FOW provides benefits such as more consistent wind patterns, minimal visual impact and greater flexibility in adhering to noise restrictions.

Current Status and Future Trajectory

FOW is at a major turning point, similar to seabed-fixed offshore wind at about a decade ago. Although floating wind technology and pilot projects have existed for over ten years, the number of FOW turbines in operation as of October 2022 is only around fifty. However, this is expected to change, with the global installed capacity of FOW estimated to surpass 5 GW by 2030 and

[1] The article was written by Labanya Prakash Jena and Prasad Ashok Thakur and was first published by the Renewable Energy Watch. https://renewablewatch.in/2023/05/24/floating-offshore-wind-a-potential-solution-to-meet-global-decarbonisation-needs/

25 GW by 2035. Additionally, the progress achieved in seabed-fixed offshore wind will accelerate the development of floating offshore wind, similar to how the offshore wind industry evolved from onshore achievements. By then, FOW projects will be designed to harness winds as distant as 300 km from coastlines at ocean depths of up to 2 km. The large-scale adoption of FOW will enable coastal geographies, often densely populated, to benefit from access to large-scale clean energy. Such an exponential transition will entail innovative approaches to improve technical designs, supply chains and excellence in project implementation spanning construction, operations and maintenance. All these require substantial investments, a policy and regulatory push, as well as ecosystem development.

Moving Toward Cost Reduction

One of the key challenges in adopting FOW is its higher cost compared to other renewable energy sources. FOW is expected to become cost competitive with the near-shore fixed-bed wind technology in the medium term. FOW facilities use hardware components that are already deployed in the fixed-bottom offshore wind, shipping and offshore oil and gas sectors; this compatibility will save additional capital investment in creating new infrastructure exclusively for FOW farms. Other key drivers for cost optimisation are a reduction in turbine costs, floating platforms and opex. Leveraging such advantages is critical, as per the IEA's Offshore Wind Outlook 2019. It describes a scenario where one in every nine new offshore wind turbines could be a floating one by 2035.

Success of FOW Pilots: Giant Strides in Clean Energy

Globally, the number of FOW pilot projects is growing rapidly, especially in advanced countries. In the US, plans are unfolding to tender out FOW sites around northern and central California, followed by the state of Oregon and the Gulf of Maine. These initiatives are envisaged to be a part of the country's plans for installing 15 GW of FOW by 2035. In the UK, the eastern coast of Scotland hosts two FOW facilities at present. This is in line with the FOW market estimate of 20 GW in the North Sea area in the medium term. Future opportunities are also being explored in England and Wales. The world's first floating wind turbine in Norway has been operational for about 15 years. The Government of Norway aims to work with the private sector to commission 4.5 GW of FOW in the near future. Across the world, Japan's Offshore Wind Promotional Law provides a favourable policy framework for FOW auction processes. Accordingly, the country organised the world's first FOW auction to commission a 16.8 MW farm. In nearby South Korea, six private players have joined hands to fulfil the target of installing 7.5 GW of FOW near the coastal city of Ulsan. As FOW technology grows, it can be the harbinger of energy independence for several regions of the world. It is hoped that, over time, the benefits of FOW will be shared across borders. Simultaneously, it can become a tool to deliver climate justice to least developed countries (LDCs) and Small Island Developing States.

Creating a Conducive Policy and Regulatory Environment

It may not be practical to anticipate that floating offshore wind will compete directly with seabed-fixed offshore wind. Renewable energy providers can benefit from feed-in tariffs (FiTs), which offer a reliable and transparent revenue source. FiT reduces the risk for developers that are unsure if they can generate enough revenue to cover the project cost throughout the investment lifetime. Floating wind energy requires substantial investment to progress from commercial demonstration to market maturity, making the revenue stability provided by FiT payments especially advantageous. FiTs can promote investment and reduce technology costs by fostering economies of scale and learning by doing, particularly in these areas. A reverse auction, which considers market development and the falling cost of technology, is the best FiT mechanism. Policymakers open a market for a fixed quantity of FOW and developers bid competitively. This approach avoids administrative price setting, resulting in potentially greater cost efficiency.

It is important to avoid pitting the two technologies, offshore wind and FOW technologies, against each other too early in tenders or seabed auctions, as this could hinder the development of the latter. Instead, introducing floating wind through dedicated tenders or supportive mechanisms until it can compete on equal terms with more established technologies would be better.

The renewable portfolio standard (RPS) is another regulatory mechanism to increase renewable energy production. Since it is technology-neutral, nascent and expensive technologies are out of favour. This crowds out potential new industries, including FOW and forecloses potential supply chain or soft cost breakthroughs. The alternative is to create a carve-out for FOW. This entails specifying a portion of the overall RPS that must be fulfilled using FOW. RPS can increase the deployment of FOW technology, resulting in a rapid price reduction of the technology.

Long-term certainty is the key for both FiTs and RPS. With FiTs, it is essential to provide a reasonable compensation period for FOW investors, ensuring they receive a fair return on their investments. Similarly, long-term targets should be established under the RPS to allow FOW investors to recover their return on investments.

Need for Skill Development

The development of floating wind technology will require the acquisition of new skill sets and the establishment of new supply chains, particularly in the design, production, handling and installation of floating foundations, mooring lines and dynamic array cables. With the expected build-out of seabed-fixed offshore wind in the near to mid-term and the rapid expansion of FOW, the market may face a shortage of relevant skill sets and suppliers. Therefore, there is an urgent need to develop the necessary skills. This can be achieved by partnering with engineering colleges and skill training institutions.

Public-Private Partnership

In order to maximise the benefits of FOW, it is important to tackle various obstacles. One of these challenges is to establish standardisation and commoditisation of the technology as well as scale up the supply chain to bring down costs. To achieve this, partnerships between public and private entities are necessary. For example, private companies can handle the design, production and development of offshore wind farms while public sector entities can create supportive port infrastructure to evacuate energy.

As FOW evolves to become a bankable solution to the world's decarbonisation needs, a holistic ecosystem approach can help countries in balancing the needs of diverse stakeholders by empowering them to become a part of the global green energy transition. Strategic competencies must be summoned to integrate FOW into our shared future.

Floating Offshore Wind – India's Next Renewable Energy Technology Frontier[1]

India's exclusive economic zone (EEZ) is estimated to be more than 2.3 million square kilometres. As per the Territorial Waters, Continental Shelf, Exclusive Economic Zone and Other Maritime Zones Act, 1976, India has sovereign rights for the purpose of producing energy from tides, winds and currents. Analysing these facts in tandem with India's resolute commitment to installing 500 GW of non-fossil fuels-based capacity by 2030 and achieving Net-Zero by 2070, reveals that Floating Offshore Wind (FOW) can usher in a new energy revolution for the country. FOW can unlock an abundant, cost-effective and reliable source of clean energy while simultaneously solving the pestering challenge of diverting large swaths of land for giga-scale clean energy projects. As the world looks for diversifying its energy basket, India's multi-faceted innovation prowess should rise to the occasion and provide global leadership in the FOW space.

Diversifying India's Clean Energy Basket

FOW constitutes wind turbines affixed on floating platforms. Through mooring lines, such platforms are anchored to the ocean floor. By design, such installations can emerge as some of the largest rotating machines ever constructed. It is well understood that India's near-term renewable energy deployment is expected to be dominated by land-based solar and wind installations with some instances of nearshore fixed wind power plants. However, India's new energy future should have a diverse mix of clean energy sources in order to achieve and possibly exceed its Net-Zero 2070 targets. FOW can emerge as a versatile addition to this mix. Coincidentally, the majority of India's coastal areas are densely populated and highly industrialised, thus providing a ready demand for future FOW power plants. FOW can also ease land-use optimisation pressure in a country where the eco-sensitive western and eastern ghat regions harbour some of the most diverse and endangered life forms on the planet. FOW can carve out a niche for itself in the evolving clean energy technology spectrum due to his attribute.

[1] The article was written by Labanya Prakash Jena, Vaibhav Chaudhary and Prasad Ashok Thakur and was first published by the ET Energy World (From the *Economic Times*). https://energy.economictimes.indiatimes.com/news/renewable/floating-offshore-wind-indias-next-renewable-energy-technology-frontier/99091249

Collaboration can usher the Adoption of FOW

As a start, India must constitute a cross-functional study of its offshore wind potential that can be harnessed in the high seas within its EEZ. Such areas are too deep for the foundations of 'fixed-bottom' wind turbines secured to the ocean floor. Here, organisations like the National Institute of Wind Energy, India Meteorological Department, ISRO, Indian Navy, etc., can add interdisciplinary value. Based on these findings, a comprehensive strategy for harnessing wind energy over the ocean deeps through FOW can be framed. Globally, developed countries have already begun such exercises. USA's Department of Energy (USADOE) states that FOW can usher in USA's green energy future by harnessing about 3 terawatts of potential power. This exceeds the current US electricity demand by a factor of two.

Leveraging Economics of Scale

USADOE estimates that at a commercial scale, the costs of the first few FOW projects can be more than 50 per cent higher compared to the costs of fixed-bottom offshore wind. However, FOW projects can be positioned in areas with higher average wind speeds. Hence the capacity factor can thus be improved and lead to increased electricity generation. To validate the same, some countries in Asia and Europe have begun phased implementation of pilot projects, while simultaneously evaluating the deployment of larger projects. As with any new technology innovation, the levelised cost of electricity (LCOE) associated with FOW seems to be higher than land based clean energy power plants at present. However, as the world witnesses a drastic reduction in the costs/unit of nearshore fixed wind power plants, FOW is also expected to trace a similar trajectory and can in the medium term become cost competitive with other solutions. Here, 'Made in India' FOW solutions can bridge the gap. In compliance with its 'Zero Effect, Zero Defect' targets, an ecosystem for high-quality, cost-competitive and environmentally benign world class products can be manufactured. This can create new export opportunities based on the foundations of affordable LCOE and India's robust project-management and information-technology prowess for commissioning clean energy projects. Thus, the goal to shrink the cost of FOW to about 30 per cent of its present value by 2035, to a range of USD 40–50 per megawatt-hour, can be achieved.

Seamless Execution Towards Giga-scale Facilities

As the global FOW knowledge base develops, India should put in place a transparent and welcoming regulatory regime for the sector. Despite this, in the early stages, it may be successful in executing only a minor fraction of the country's vast FOW potential. However, it will still have the capability of making a large difference in the lives of tens of millions of citizens in the coastal areas. To ensure steadfast forward movement from pilot projects to gigawatt-scale facilities requires a 'one-team' approach across governments, businesses, academia, startups and civil society. Such an initiative can expedite the creation of targeted programmes to achieve breakthroughs in this sector. Any investments in FOW will directly contribute to the advancement of turbine efficiency, reduced ecological footprint and improved transmission and pooling facilities, resulting in lower LCOE. It can also trigger developments in adjacent sectors like meteorology, remote sensing and supercomputing for creating high-accuracy planetary weather forecast models in the context of a rapidly warming planet.

New Energy – New Skills

FOW can create viable resettlement options for the workforce deployed oil & gas sector whose jobs may get adversely impacted due to global decarbonisation initiatives. Experienced and fresh workforce can be skilled for this new energy technology as it is expected to create good-paying jobs in a growing clean energy-based global economy. A cross-pollination of ideas between sectors can also help in repurposing billions of dollars' worth of existing offshore O&G infrastructure for applications like FOW, offshore green hydrogen or ammonia manufacturing, storage, transportation and refuelling for the global shipping industry. It can provide a new lease of life to the economics or Small Island Developing States (SIDS) and littoral Least Developed Countries (LDCs). The creation of local green jobs through opportunities in FOW can be a good start toward achieving climate justice for the populations that have contributed the least but are impacted the most by the deterioration of our planet's climatic balance.

India's present focus on large-scale terrestrial clean energy projects entails solving for multifaced issues related to land-use management. Often, this leads to increased LCOE and delayed execution of clean energy facilities. Here, FOW can emerge as a panacea that has the potential to rapidly decarbonise India's economy while making clean energy affordable.

Net-Zero: Harnessing India's Geothermal Energy Potential[1]

As India races towards its target of achieving 'energy-independence' by 2047, its energy basket is progressively getting dominated by renewable energy sources like solar, wind, biomass and hydro energy. A versatile addition to this mix can be Geothermal Energy (GTE). This energy form is clean, safe and sustainable as the hot water extracted from the earth is injected back to the geothermal reservoir after utilising its heat content. GTE is available round the clock and is agnostic to the availability and intensity of sunlight, local weather conditions and seasons of the year. These characteristics make it ideal for supporting use cases like power generation for baseload demands, heating and cooling within the low-medium temperature band. In suitable circumstances, GTE can mitigate the demand for electricity through its direct use and Ground Source Heat Pumps (GSHP).

Understanding GTE Projects

The earth's crust contains hydrothermal systems that have stored heat that typically manifests itself in the form of geysers and hot springs. Drilling activities in hot spring areas yield geothermal fluids at high temperatures and pressures. This fluid typically contains steam varying from 0 to almost 100 per cent. Energy is extracted from this hot and pressurised fluid plus steam concoction. For a GTE project, drilling of wells is necessary, both for production and reinjection of hot fluids. This ensures that withdrawn resources are returned back to the earth. Setting up a holistic and sustainable GTE project also entails water conservation and watershed management through forest cover. The GTE extracted can be further deployed for electricity generation and heating. The site characteristics of geothermal activity and the type of technology deployed typically dictates the quantum of electricity that can be generated from a GTE project. Indian geothermal resources are mostly medium enthalpy type, hence technical viability of sites can be conclusively established only after pilot demonstration projects yield

[1] The article was written by Labanya Prakash Jena and Prasad Ashok Thakur and was first published by the ET Energy World (From the Economic Times). https://energy.economictimes.indiatimes.com/news/renewable/net-zero-harnessing-indias-geothermal-potential/105523856

satisfactory yields. Geothermal Power (GP) plants can be designed to be modular and can be installed in incremental units. Thus, it is well-suited for fulfilling the energy demands of remote/interior populations as Kilo Watt (kW) scale plants are also feasible.

India's GTE Potential

The Renewable Capacity Statistics 2023 states that 14.88 Gigawatts (GW) Geothermal Power (GP) has been installed globally till date. This may ramp up to up to 16.77 GW by 2025 with a potential to reach 23.74 GW by end of this decade. The Geological Survey of India has shortlisted about 350 high potential sites across the country based on their hot-spring activity. It is theoretically estimated that 10 GW of power can be extracted from known sources till date. Some of the important geothermal provinces are situated in the Himalayan region, the Western Coastal region, Son-Narmada-Tapi (SONATA) basin, Godavari basin, etc. Moreover, opportunities to develop direct heat applications (like GSHP) across the country can effectively cut down the need for fossil fuels for day-to-day heating requirements for domestic and small-medium industrial use cases. Here, the proactive contribution of technical agencies of various state governments can mobilise the private sector, startups and academia to leverage this opportunity.

GP Economics

It is observed that GP projects are capital intensive but have very low operating costs. The characteristics of the geothermal field at site influence the cost of a GP project. The major cost components include exploration of resources, assessment, drilling of wells for production and injection purposes, site specific infrastructure, networks for management of geothermal fluids including their collection and disposal, grid connection costs and project development costs. The 'Renewable Power Generation Costs 2021' report published by IRENA suggest the global weighted average installed capital cost of GP was USD 3991/kW. The Levelised Cost of Electricity (LCOE) varies from USD 0.04 to USD 0.14 per kWh with and economic life of approximately twenty-five years and a capacity factor/plant load factor of around 75 per cent. As per the United States Department of Energy, attempts are underway to reduce the capital cost of GP by 90 per cent by the year 2035 by achieving about 40 GW capacity deployment in that country.

Accelerating GP in India

To accelerate the deployment of this novel decarbonisation solution, it is critical to promote cross-functional collaboration in technology, financing, policy and skill-development.

Co-creation of novel financial models for long tenure loans stretching up to thirty years, milestone-based repayment cycles and creation of unique risk-return expectations are critical enablers. High-risk public capital during exploration stage (when risk is highest for investors), credit guarantee and insurance can reduce riskiness of GP project thereby attract a large amount of private capital at an affordable rate. Therefore, India aims to permit up to 100 per cent Foreign Direct Investment (FDI) for GP projects. Feed-in-tariffs and heat purchase agreement can also be explored which can mitigate revenue generation risks for GP projects.

Investing in research and development (R&D) focused on manufacturing customised drilling equipment can significantly extend the operational lifespans of these tools while simultaneously mitigating uncertainties in drilling outcomes. Such strategic R&D initiatives have the potential to make a substantial impact on cost reduction in geothermal projects. In line with the nascent GP industry's demand, drilling activities conducted for exploratory purposes can be treated as per the R&D policy of the Ministry of New and Renewable Energy (Govt. of India). Government grants and viability gap funding instruments can also to be extended for promising technologies. Permissions to diversify the balance sheets of GP companies by allowing them to utilise by-products resulting from exploration activities, especially the rare earth minerals, can encourage accelerated investments in this sector. Government grants and viability gap funding instruments can also be extended for promising technologies.

It is also necessary to impart technical and project management expertise in critical areas like geosciences, drilling, reservoir engineering, remote sensing, etc., to create a sustained talent pipeline. Government and private sector centres of excellence and international institutions can provide technical assistance and knowledge sharing platforms to support such endeavours. GTE is literally an infinite and clean energy treasure buried beneath our feet. The time is now ripe to step up efforts in research, innovation and commercialisation of enhanced solutions to 'unearth it' and dispatch it for decarbonising our heating and electric systems.

Clean Goals: Decarbonising India's Industrial Heating[1]

In India, the industries sector is second only to the electricity-generation sector when it comes to energy-related carbon dioxide emissions, as per International Energy Agency estimates. The sector also contributed to 41 per cent of the country's electricity consumption during 2021–22, thus causing indirect carbon emissions. Hence, decarbonising India's industrial sector is critical for reducing the emissions intensity of its GDP by 45 per cent by 2030 and achieving its net-zero target for 2070.

Understanding Industrial Heat

Manufacturing activities form a major share of the energy consumption within the industrial sector. It includes all facilities and hardware involved in the production, processing and assembly of diverse commodities. As expected, this encompasses a wide array of operations within its ambit. Globally, applying heat is a standard process across industries to transform the properties of materials. These include modification of chemical and physical characteristics of raw materials such as dehydration, facilitating chemical reactions, treating alloys and metals, liquefication of polymers, etc. Such intense industrial heat requirement is responsible for most of the GHG emissions in the manufacturing value chain as it is presently sourced primarily from fossil fuels like coal, petroleum-based fuels and natural gas.

Technological Solutions are Available to Replace or Optimise Industrial Heat

Adopting low/zero-carbon fuels and electrical heating systems can reduce industrial heating's greenhouse gas (GHG) footprint. The adoption of AI-enabled smart energy automation tools and digital twin models where relevant can optimise thermal cycles of generation and energy conservation. Developing new chemistries can churn out materials with

---

[1] The article was written by Prasad Ashok Thakur and Labanya Prakash Jena, and originally published on the Renewable Energy Watch, https://renewablewatch.in/2023/10/08/clean-goals-decarbonising-indias-industrial-heating/#:~:text=Hence%2C%20decarbonising%20India's%20industrial%20sector,net%20zero%20target%20for%2-02070.&text=Manufacturing%20activities%20form%20a%20major,consumption%20within%20the%20industrial%20sector.

physical and chemical properties, reducing the need for industrial heating processes. Deploying electromagnetic radiations like microwaves/radio frequencies, mechanical vibrations through contact/non-contact ultrasound, biotechnological approaches and advanced membranes for ultrafiltration/reverse osmosis reduces industrial heat requirements. The heat recovery and reuse philosophy can drive research in creating circular energy loops within industrial systems. This approach emphasises the development/use of new materials and in-situ energy reserves for calibrated heat injection mechanisms to limit thermal losses. Novel Industry 4.0 approaches like additive manufacturing/3D printing can significantly reduce the number of thermal processing steps.

Decarbonising Industrial Heat

Realising the growing importance of the manufacturing sector in the country's trajectory towards a $5 trillion economy, concerted efforts must be made to reduce carbon emissions from energy-intensive processes like industrial heating. A dedicated mission can be conceived to collect and analyse empirical datasets about India's present industrial heat requirements across sectors. Based on short/mid/long term sectoral forecasts, developing a portfolio of emission reduction solutions for different use cases of industrial heat must be set into motion. Attention must be given to the evolving dynamics of large, micro-small and medium industries and startups to ensure the widespread percolation of such innovations. Drawing inspiration from the United States Department of Energy's (US-DOE) 'Industrial Heat Shot' initiative (85 per cent GHG reduction by 2035), the mission should set ambitious and time-bound targets based on transparent consultations with relevant stakeholders. India should aim to develop cost-competitive, planet-friendly and reliable industrial heat decarbonisation solutions for the domestic and global markets. Such initiatives can help improve the competitiveness of India's manufacturing sector while meeting our nationally determined contribution (NDC) targets.

Roadmap for Execution

Commercially available or near-commercialised solutions must be quickly evaluated and adopted by industrial-heat process owners to get near-term relief for addressing the challenges of high energy consumption and resulting GHG emissions. Opportunities for replacing polluting technologies within existing plant infrastructure that require relatively low effort and costs must be seized immediately. Here, reduction of energy losses, waste heat recovery and smart energy automation solutions are some areas worth exploring. Additionally, government agencies at union/state/local levels working on industry-related matters can take the first step by creating awareness and financially supporting quick-win pilot demonstrations, with a special focus on MSMEs. Online and certified platforms can be launched to model and evaluate competing technology solutions to promote informed decision-making. In line with global mega-trends, financial incentives/deterrents like tax rebates, upskilling-workforce through government-supported MOOC courses, selective imposition of carbon tax, awards and recognitions can be strategically used to hand-hold all stakeholders to embark collectively on the industrial heat decarbonisation pathway.

In the medium term, large-scale clean alternative fuels/energy sources (for example, solar/wind/bio energy-based electricity, green hydrogen, geothermal, etc.) for industrial heat applications are expected to offer cost advantages. This may entail significant modifications to in-situ infrastructure and its paraphernalia. Suitable financial incentives and policy frameworks must be introduced to support this transition for hard-to-abate sectors like cement, steel and refining. In the long term, it is envisaged that transformative changes in processing facilities and the creation of novel raw materials may limit the requirement of thermal heating to selective product value chains.

CSIR can Play a Critical Role

The Council of Scientific & Industrial Research (CSIR) can act as a nodal agency to catalyse such efforts. CSIR has developed cutting-edge capabilities and a pan-India reach through its network of national laboratories/outreach centres. It can become the trusted platform for incubating strategic public private-academia partnerships for solving techno commercial challenges supporting industrial heat decarbonisation efforts. Such R&D and the subsequent scale-up activities can be centred around end user-inspired themes.

Direct Air Capture: How to Accelerate this Technology to Limit Global Warming[1]

There is only 380 $GtCO_2$ of carbon budget available to limit the earth's temperature increase by 1.5°C by 2050—a budget that, at the current pace, will be exceeded in just nine years. We still emit ~50 $GtCO_2$ every year and the CO_2 emission reduction is not materialising at the desired rate, so it is highly unlikely the 1.5°C target will be met.

Direct air capture (DAC), considered both a technology and process, deployed in tandem, is the best option to remove CO_2 from the atmosphere to limit global warming. DAC is different from conventional carbon capture, which typically implies locking in carbon molecules at the source of emissions, as it extracts CO_2 directly from the atmosphere. However, the adoption of DAC is limited. Presently, twenty-seven DAC facilities are reported to be commissioned globally, and cumulatively, they can capture about 10,000 tonnes of carbon dioxide per year, according to the International Energy Agency (IEA). Another 130 DAC facilities are thought to be in the pipeline, and it is estimated that a cumulative capacity of 75 $MtCO_2$/year will be installed—still less than 0.5 per cent of global emissions per year.

Challenges to Scaling up DAC Technology

The high cost of DAC technology is restricting its deployment—the current DAC cost is about two to six times higher than the desired cost. Capital and energy cost constitutes about 95 per cent of the cost of DAC technology. The capital costs for the DAC systems contribute to the majority of costs—in the range of \$150/tCO_2–\$1,000/tCO_2 depending on the type of technology. On the operating cost, the cost of clean energy would be in the range of \$360–620/tCO_2 while the cost of fossil fuel would be in the range of \$88–228/tCO_2. Hence there is a trade-off between a high rate of CO_2 removal—using DAC without using fossil fuel and the cost of removal. The challenge is to reduce the cost of capital and energy.

Increasing the scale of manufacturing, increasing the energy efficiency of manufacturing sub-components and utilisation of clean sources can help

---

[1] The article was written by Labanya Prakash Jena and Prasad Ashok Thakur and was first published by the World Economic Forum. https://www.weforum.org/agenda/2023/10/accelerating-direct-air-capture-technology-global-warming/

reduce DAC technology's cost. Using the learning-by-doing rules in the mass manufacturing of DAC, the cost is expected to come down rapidly. DAC facilities designed and manufactured as simple and modular knock-down units can lower costs as standardised spares can be mass-produced. On the operational expenses front, nature-based sorbents with high capture rates, efficient thermal energy regeneration coupled with waste heat utilisation and optimised air contactors are looked upon as quick wins for cost reduction. Additionally, increasing energy efficiency in the operations of a DAC facility can be a source of cost relief. Future opportunities for cost optimisation can stem from advancements in air-contactors, sorbents and design elements of DAC units. Specifically, passive air contactors are some of the recent considerations.

Financing Innovation and Scale-up of DAC Technology

DAC technologies are in their early stages of development. The business cases and economies of scale for commercial operations are yet to be conclusively established. Hence, perceived and real uncertainties constrain large private financing flows, which in turn constrains production scale. This proposed DAC fund—supported by governments and multilateral agencies—can accelerate financing for DAC technology. Since the technology is novel, a massive amount of grant capital and early-stage risky equity capital is required. A DAC fund could infuse public capital to increase the scale of operation of relevant technologies and would help funnel investment into the development of new technologies to improve unit efficiency and economics. Unlike private financers, the fund could provide risky capital on a lower or no-expected-return basis or grants wherever necessary. The fund could also invest strategically to alleviate the apprehensions of private investors. For example, public financing can be used as junior equity in DAC technology projects to reduce the riskiness of private investors.

Scaling Green Hydrogen in India: Adopting a Three-Pronged Approach[1]

As India sets its sight on achieving energy independence by 2047, Green Hydrogen (GH2) will play a critical role. Hydrogen's value proposition is most compelling when it comes to slashing down the carbon footprint of the energy sector and industries such as cement, ammonia, iron, steel, transportation and refining. It is a versatile molecule as it can be used as a potential feedstock to produce several types of synthetic fuels relevant for long-distance shipping and aviation. India's distinct advantage in low-cost renewable energy generation makes GH2 the most competitive form of hydrogen in the long run. The Government of India has provided the right impetus to the sector by announcing a Production Linked Incentive (PLI) for Green Hydrogen. It aims to significantly cut production costs associated with GH2. This paves way for GH2 to compete with, and in the medium-long term, outperform fossil fuels.

Promote the Establishment of Green Hydrogen Hubs

As we usher in the early phases of the GH2 era, the Union/State/Local governments can work in tandem with the industry to earmark or identify clusters of high demand for GH2—the green hydrogen demand hubs—for a large-scale matching of supply and demand, located in close proximity to one another. By pooling supply and demand in selected hubs, the cost of transportation, distribution and storage can be optimised. To ensure a large-scale, financially viable business case of GH2, mapping the ramp-up of GH2 supply with a corresponding and growing demand within the same region is desirable. Such co-location has immense advantages. The heavy and hard-to-decarbonise industries, often also the largest consumers of energy, are envisaged to be the prominent early adopters of GH2. This is because the cost of hydrogen can be competitive for them starting in the near future. Governments can pluck this low-hanging fruit and preferentially extend diverse incentives to GH2 manufacturers. The proposal by the government to create GH2 valleys or clusters is a positive development in this direction.

[1] The article was written by Labanya Prakash Jena and Prasad Ashok Thakur and was first published by the ET Energy World (From the *Economic Times*). https://energy.economictimes.indiatimes.com/news/renewable/scaling-green-hydrogen-in-india-adopting-a-three-pronged-approach/97037367

Digital Platform for Efficient Linkages

Secondly, governments along with the private sector can develop a 'GH2 Matchmaker (GH2M)' digital platform to facilitate hydrogen stakeholders to better connect with each other. While it becomes a virtual marketplace to match the demand-supply of GH2, there can be better coordination on transportation, storage and fuel cell development as well. GH2M allows hydrogen producers, end-users and other stakeholders to self-identify and align potential needs in specific geographic areas in real time. It can facilitate regional business development opportunities by streamlining safety codes, standards and the availability of a skilled workforce.

The GH2M can also increase awareness, acceptance and penetration of GH2 ecosystem solutions like solar/wind/clean energy generation, electrolysers and fuel cells. GH2M can too spur the development of financial products that are tailor-made for the hydrogen value chain. Presently, there are efforts made by the USA's Department of Energy to develop a digital portal on these lines to support its indigenous ecosystem. For example, the companies planning to use GH2 can enter its requirement on the portal, which will help the GH2 manufacturer and suppliers to make business decisions in that particular hub.

GH2M: Evolution of a Sophisticated Matchmaker

India's world-leading digital and ITeS prowess can turbocharge its emergence as a clean energy solutions powerhouse. A future-ready GH2M digital portal, powered by AI/ML, can have unified visibility of the supply and demand profiles of all ecosystem players. As a result, ancillary features and services like testing, labelling, tracing, certifications of origin, finance, insurance, workforce skilling, safety, etc., can create layers on top of this portal for increasing its functionality and real-world utility. It can not only help in predicting the future GH2 pricing dynamics but can also regulate it. The data points gathered and analysed using the GH2M can help it continuously evolve to be a better version of itself. As it matures, it can be deployed in planning optimal approaches to solve the evolving energy landscape in India and the globe. Anchored by India, it can attract global players to invest in the country as opportunities to leverage shared infrastructure and services exponentially compound in value. Interoperability of data from other supplementary ecosystems, such as Carbon Capture Utilisation and Storage, electricity, weather systems, etc., can be fused with GH2M, resulting in world-leading net-zero solutions ecosystems.

Global Partnerships for a Green Future

Governments across the world are introducing phase-wise Green Hydrogen Purchase Obligation (GH2PO) to provide an initial boost to the sector by setting minimum usage targets for various industries. Here, India's GH2M digital-stack-based architecture can be shared with the world. It can serve as a lighthouse to steer the development of holistic GH2 ecosystems globally. Based on the insights provided by GH2M, producers/consumers can strike cross-border partnerships and optimise their business models by aggregating supply/demand based on multi-modal production, storage and transportation. This will also prompt the evolution of consensus-based and sector-specific policies for establishing global standards in design, construction, maintenance and end-of-use infrastructure in the hydrogen value chain.

Globally, India can share its experiences in implementing nationwide GH2 programmes with other developing and least-developed countries. Such hand-holding in the initial stages can optimise the utilisation of public resources for the highest impact in resource-stressed economies of the global south.

India has always demonstrated through resolute actions that it considers the entire world as one single family. Even on highly polarising topics like equity and differentiated responsibilities in the fight against climate change, India firmly believes that it can win only when the entire world wins. As the world's clean energy gameplan intensifies, India's development of a successful GH2M ecosystem can be a masterstroke that helps humanity win.

Breaking Barriers: Reducing Electrolysis Costs to Fast-Track Green Hydrogen Integration[1]

As the world transitions towards decarbonising its economy, green hydrogen (GH2) is expected to play a pivotal role—a magic energy storage solution, low-carbon industrial energy and feedstock, a low-carbon fuel for long-distance vehicles such as trucks, shipping and airlines and green fertiliser. International Renewable Energy Agency (IRENA) forecasts that GH2 will account for up to 12 per cent of the final energy consumption by 2050. However, there is a challenge to adopting GH2. It is more expensive than grey hydrogen generated by using coal and natural gas. Green hydrogen costs \$4 to \$7 per kg versus \$2 to \$6 per kg for grey hydrogen. This cost depends on the cost of energy—a decline in the price of renewable energy, the energy source of GH2, will further reduce the cost of green hydrogen.

After renewable energy, the second highest-cost component of GH2 is the electrolyser. The mass adoption of GH2 hinges on the rapid decline of the cost of renewable energy and electrolysers. While the cost of renewable energy has declined significantly, the cost of electrolysers is still very high. Hence, it is important to reduce the cost of electrolysers as quickly as possible to accelerate the adoption of GH2 in the energy system.

Understanding Electrolyser Technologies

Consider the current technological progress of the electrolyser. None of the presently available solutions is suitable for commercial-scale GH2 manufacturing at competitive costs compared to the H2 produced using hydrocarbons (coal and natural gas). There are four electrolyser technologies that can potentially turn around the tables shortly. These are alkaline systems (AS), proton exchange membrane (PEM), solid oxide electrolyser cell (SOEC) and anion exchange membrane (AEM). AS offers the largest system size or the lowest cost per unit. However, its limitations include a 'high minimum load', which makes it intolerant to the variable nature of power

[1] The article was written by Labanya Prakash Jena and Prasad Ashok Thakur and was first published by the ET Energy World (From the *Economic Times*). https://energy.economictimes.indiatimes.com/news/renewable/breaking-barriers-reducing-electrolysis-costs-to-fast-track-green-hydrogen-integration/106971835

sourced from renewables. Here, PEM electrolysers have significantly better credentials—this technology quickly ramps up and down, so they can absorb intermittent energy sources such as solar and wind. In addition, they are easy to maintain, reliable, simpler to use and more efficient in converting electric power into GH2. However, PEM electrolysers are far more expensive due to the use of platinum group catalytic chemicals—a costly material produced in a few places. With the present technological advancements, companies have not found a low-cost alternative material, although the volume of platinum required per unit of electrolyser is dropping rapidly. AEM systems can help in solving this cost challenge. However, they are presently in the nascent stages of commercial application. SOEC systems are also riddled with similar challenges pertaining to costs and lack of large-scale market viability.

Opportunities for Cost Rationalisation

The pathway for cost reduction of electrolysers is to find alternative materials for manufacturing PEM and SOEC electrolysers. Further investment in research and development (R&D) is required to find alternative materials to platinum. In addition, electrolyser efficiency can be improved further by increasing the capacity of electrolyser systems to boost the throughput. Besides, further investment in R&D is required to increase the usable life of the stacks, a key cost component of electrolysers, especially for AEM electrolysers.

Drawing inference from the solar and wind clean energy generation sector, the accumulating large-scale production and deployment experience with electrolysers is expected to reduce system costs. According to Bloomberg, the learning rate for AEM and PEM electrolysers is 18 per cent and 20 per cent, respectively. This means that doubling the production quantity of these systems will reduce costs by nearly 20 per cent. However, private investors are not committing themselves to so much investment as the profitability of electrolyser production is still in the negative territory. Here, policy plays a critical role in accelerating adoption instead of waiting for the private financers that will come gradually.

Policy Support—the Need to Front-load Public Investment

The European Union (EU), the USA and Australia have set up dedicated financing mechanisms to promote the constituent manufacturing value chain of GH2 and its derivatives. Governments have also directly supported electrolyser manufacturing by floating open competitive tenders, with the

EU's 40 GW electrolyser manufacturing tender being a showcase example. GH2 purchase obligations imposed on hard-to-abate sectors like cement, steel, oil, gas and so on, are also being directed to support the advancement of electrolyser technologies. According to an International Energy Agency (IEA) report, only 3 GW of electrolyser capacity is estimated to be installed globally by the end of 2023. If the world realises the global net-zero emissions target by 2050, an installed electrolyser capacity of more than 550 GW by 2030 is desirable. This indicates that the current government's support is not enough and needs to ramp up quickly.

Policymakers can support in two ways to reduce the cost of electrolysers: massive incentives for R&D and acceleration of production volume. Incentives can be in the form of tax exemptions, grants, subsidies, concessional capital and even equity investment. Governments can offer long-term concession debt financing, grants, or viability gap funding for electrolyser production to make it commercially viable. The government can also become an entrepreneurial financer and provide equity capital for electrolyser production and exit from the investment when the business is profitable and can attract private capital at a reasonable rate. Similarly, governments can incentivise massive R&D to find alternative and low-cost materials for electrolyser manufacturing. Governments can also become venture equity capital providers to support small-size companies conducting R&D to reduce the cost of electrolyser manufacturing.

Partnerships Can Scale Up Production Quickly

Apart from innovations in the realm of technology, electrolyser ecosystems can significantly reduce their 'landed cost' by creating efficient supply chains of sub-components and their constituent chemicals, new GH2 demand centres and tailor-made business models for critical applications. Partnerships among electrolyser manufacturers can accelerate further development of this equipment. Here, countries can create 'green partnerships' for collectively leapfrogging to a future powered by affordable, clean and resilient energy systems. History suggests that when competitors join hands to accelerate the development of an industry, it's a win-win situation for everyone in the industry.

Future Ready: How can We Create a World-class Green Hydrogen Delivery Network for India?[1]

In the context of India's aim to achieve energy independence by 2047 and net-zero by 2070, green hydrogen is increasingly gaining prominence. With an ambition to cater to global and domestic green hydrogen needs, the country aims to manufacture 5 million tonnes per annum by 2030. It has launched a National Green Hydrogen Mission (NGHM) to bridge the gap between the concept and commissioning of its green hydrogen projects.

Though the green hydrogen ecosystem is in its nascent stages, it is turbocharged by several initiatives from the supply and demand sides. The government declared a funding outlay of approximately $2.25 billion. Out of which the government announced in June 2023 to allocate approximately $1.6 billion for green hydrogen production and approximately $0.5 billion for domestic manufacturing of electrolyser—a key component of the green hydrogen supply chain. Prominent among them are production-linked incentives (PLI), waiver of inter-state transmission system (ISTS) charges for green hydrogen manufacturing and commitment of facilitation of its uptake in sectors like refining, steel, shipping, fertilisers, road/rail mobility and city gas distribution.

Since the target is ambitious India needs its governments, corporates, startups and academia to work in tandem to enable this energy transformation. However, the development of a fully integrated, user-friendly and cost-effective value chain entails the creation of a future ready green hydrogen delivery and storage infrastructure.

Understanding Green Hydrogen Delivery: Connecting Supply with Demand

Hydrogen is the lightest element. Its molecule has low volumetric energy density. To transport large quantities of green hydrogen, it must be either pressurised or liquefied. Due to these reasons, creating green hydrogen delivery networks costs more than conventional fuels while resulting in

[1] The article was written by Labanya Prakash Jena and Prasad Ashok Thakur and was first published by the Renewable Watch. https://renewablewatch.in/2023/08/01/future-ready-how-can-we-create-a-world-class-green-hydrogen-delivery-network-for-india/

some safety challenges. In gaseous form, after passing through reciprocating/rotary/ionic/centrifugal compressors, it is transported in tube trailers and pipelines. Presently, India's existing hydrogen delivery infrastructure has limited and specialised commercial deployment; refining, fertilisers and metals manufacturing sectors serving as its core custodians.

As envisaged in the NGHM, delivery of Green Hydrogen from production or storage sites to their points of consumption at scale, in a safe and cost-effective manner will emerge as a critical infrastructure requirement in the near future. Hence, the development of new technologies like chemistry-based molecule carriers for high-density green hydrogen transport is the need of the hour. Here, some emerging solutions include metal hydrides, carbon nanostructures and reversible hydrocarbons. The infrastructure gap that must be bridged includes fibre-reinforced polymer pipelines (FRP) networks for catering to large and stable demand centres. Other facilities include liquefaction equipment, cryogenic liquid tanker trucks, vehicle-mounted and ground mounted cascades, high-capacity compressors and specialised dispensers working in tandem with contaminant detectors, purification technologies and smart meters. To start with, such capabilities can support large-scale green hydrogen uptake in centres like industrial complexes, electricity generation assets, city-based cooking-gas distribution hubs and retail outlets for mobility sectors. Some intangible enablers that can fortify the exponential uptake trajectories include planning region and application specific green hydrogen expansion roadmaps empowered by real-time digital matchmaking solutions. Such an approach can streamline supply and demand dynamics for optimum utilisation of the delivery infrastructure.

Managing Risks: Key to Unlock Finance for Green Hydrogen Delivery

Green hydrogen projects often encounter challenging financing conditions from financing entities because of the many real and perceived risks associated with them. The situation is further aggravated as presently, there are not enough numbers of commercial-scale operational projects from where financers can derive confidence and experience. Moreover, investors are adopting a 'wait and watch' approach as the requirements of capital expenditure are relatively large vis-à-vis the real and perceived risks. Therefore, they may consider other green projects in solar/wind/bioenergy, electrification of industrial processes and energy efficiency as relatively better investment opportunities.

In the context of green hydrogen projects, there are risks from both revenue and cost of operation. The uncertain volume of supply emanating from the lack of certainty on offtake duration and volume and price-points in the context of cyclical business environments make delivery infrastructure business highly risky. Besides, the uncertainty in the maturity of technology, lack of predictable maintenance and operations expenditures make the cost of operation less predictable. To turn the tables in favour of green hydrogen projects, the above risks must be reduced to a level that can attract private financiers to invest in green hydrogen projects.

As elaborated in the NGHM, an initial stimulus from a few major public and private sector entities in the country may substantially scale up the interest in deploying a large number of green hydrogen projects in the near future. This is expected to provide a fillip to all constituent elements of its value chain. Building on the foundations of indigenous innovation and economies of scale in design, manufacturing and customer services, a virtuous cycle of cost-competitive and high-quality green hydrogen offerings is expected to be set into motion.

Catering to Demand: Nationally and Globally

The key goals of the upcoming green hydrogen delivery ecosystem include the reduction of costs, improving energy delivery efficiency, ensuring the purity of green hydrogen and achieving zero-leakage networks. From a systems perspective, for each green hydrogen application and demand region, fact-based models must be created to assess the trade-offs between green hydrogen manufacturing options and its last-mile delivery opportunities. Such an approach is in line with NGHM and the creation of green hydrogen hubs/valleys/clusters that can pool-in resources and contribute towards building a national green hydrogen delivery masterplan. The federal structure of our country can be leveraged to create inter-state networks that can lead to the creation of a vibrant national grid. Such successful solutions and giga-scale programme management experiences can then be shared with other partner countries to help the world embark on a sustainable, rapid and inclusive growth trajectory.

Green Hydrogen Needs Concessional Finance[1]

Green hydrogen (GH2) is fast emerging as a winner in the race to become an energy-transition solution. A recent *Financial Times* report estimates that this transition will entail investments worth $20 trillion by 2050. India's National Green Hydrogen Mission (NGHM) is expected to play a pivotal role in propelling the country towards achieving energy independence by 2047 and net-zero by 2070. It can contribute towards achieving technological sovereignty. NGHM aims to generate 5 million tonnes per annum (mtpa), with an investment of $200 billion by 2030—with an outlay of just $2.25 billion by the government. The government announced in June that it will allocate $1.6 billion for green hydrogen production and $0.5 billion for domestic manufacturing of electrolyser—a key link in the green hydrogen supply chain. With the government pitching in with just $2.25 billion, mobilising the quantum required ($200 billion) will need collective efforts. Open communications channel with the stakeholders can help identify and address regulatory/policy inconsistencies as well as challenges for investment.

Giga-scale GH2 projects are complex and yet to be executed in India. Currently, the technology maturity and commercial viability of the constituent elements remain to be verified. Firstly, considering the present costs associated with obtaining reliable, clean energy, seawater treatment and electrolysers, the production of GH2 is costlier than grey-H2. Secondly, the shortfall of cost-efficient transportation and storage infrastructure like pipelines/liquefication facilities/GH2 cascades linking the production and consumption centres must be bridged. Alternatives of using ammonia or other fuel carriers for shipping may become viable but are not fully established at this stage. The use-cases/application portfolio of GH2 has some more distance to go before it can stand the test of scale and technology maturity, as demonstrated in the present state of fuel cells and green steel/cement sectors. Moreover, many early-stage investors flag that the lack of a clear and consistent 'green-premium' monetising regime for GH2 limits their willingness and ability to make strategic commitments to the sector.

---

[1] The article was written by Labanya Prakash Jena and Prasad Thakur and was first published by the *Financial Express*. https://www.financialexpress.com/opinion/green-hydrogen-needs-concessional-finance/3150575/

A recent collation of investors' perspectives by the European Investment Bank on stimulating investment for the GH2 sector identifies the risks emanating from fluctuating offtake prices, mismatch in the duration of offtake commitments (typically 5–7 years at a time) vis-à-vis life cycles of GH2 manufacturing assets (about 25 years), industrial cycles dictating offtake volumes and operational risks related to efficiency and reliability of GH2 equipment as key concerns. In the Indian context, potential delays in land acquisition, environmental clearances and construction of GH2 facilities, liquefaction plants and pipelines are also relevant. Due to the lack of an integrated framework for demand generation, there are no predictable revenue streams. Presently, there are limited consumers in India who enter into bespoke offtake agreements to buy H2 at non-transparent price points. All these dynamics make green hydrogen risky from the perspective of commercial financers.

In this early stage of development, public sector grants and other forms of concessionary funding will be a critical source of project financing until sufficient private sector funding sources are available. Blending public and private capital is key to making green hydrogen projects bankable and commercially viable. Multilateral Development Banks (MDBs) and Development Financial Institutions (DFIs) can fund projects, even if the economics are uncertain or the risk is high. They can offer concessional debt capital or equity capital to improve the risk-return profile of individual investments. The concessional capital can bridge the existing financing gap and consequently create a market. As the GH2 projects mature and investors are willing to participate, DFIs and MDBs can exit from their equity investments.

Investors across the globe have expressed their demand for creating a level playing field by pronouncing the long-term government strategies on topics like 'carbon levy'. Such a measure can ascribe a value to the negative impacts of non-GH2 products/processes. Moreover, lack of clarity on 'additionality requirements' that take an integrated view of clean energy and GH2 sectors, silence on standards for health, safety and environment (HSE) and a lack of synchronous policy frameworks between India's key trading partner countries are some of the teething concerns dampening the investor sentiments.

India can break the vicious cycle of financial paucity for its GH2 initiatives by introducing volume- and price-based incentives for providing an early stimulus to the ecosystem. Such frameworks can bridge viability gaps to create a conducive environment for green entrepreneurs as the country undergoes a clean energy transition. It can improve the access-to-finance for high-potential indigenous GH2 innovations by crafting GH2 financing mechanisms within its flagship publicly funded programmes. Typical examples include setting up a dedicated innovation fund governed by an expert council for promoting GH2 projects. It can also leverage the National Investment and Infrastructure Fund to provide early-stage support to dedicated GH2 venture capital funds-led equity investments while topping it up with GH2-tailored advisory solutions.

Constructive interventions can ignite an institutionalised impetus for unleashing the true market potential of GH2 in diverse sectors.

5 Ways to Make Green Hydrogen Available Around the World[1]

Green hydrogen (GH2) is expected to become the next-gen, low-carbon solution to decarbonise hard-to-abate industries, long-distance transportation and the agriculture sector. All the large economies, including the USA, China, Japan, Germany and India, are betting on GH2 to reduce their carbon footprints. It is worth noting that such countries have announced significant investments in GH2 with in-built provisions to cater to the large export demand firming up rapidly.

Unlike renewable energy, GH2 derivatives are expected to be convenient to store and supply even at long distances. As per the International Energy Agency (IEA), the development of GH2 markets is an important step towards enhancing the transition of world energy security and clean energy. Presently, the global GH2 ecosystem is in its nascent stages—and hence, it is important to lay the foundations of an efficient, transparent and equitable trading ecosystem to enable reaching net zero as early as possible.

Slash Trade Barriers

Trade-related costs will be a critical component that influences the development of global supply chains for GH2. As per a recent WTO-IRENA report, the average applied tariff rate on H2 (all hydrogen, including green) is around 5.3 per cent in most WTO members, higher than for ammonia (4.4 per cent) and methanol (5 per cent). As of December 2023, only thirty-eight countries allowed duty-free trade of H2, forty-seven for ammonia and fifty-three for methanol. Supporting the flow of goods and services relevant to the GH2 value chain through a low-cost trade regime is equally important to stimulate the emergence of a globally integrated and standardised GH2 market. In this area, only eighteen countries allow for the duty-free trade of fuel cells, twenty-five for compressors, twenty-three for H2-compliant steel containers, forty-eight for H2-compliant pipelines and sixty-three for electrolysers. Thus, one may conclude that there are mountains to move in this domain.

[1] The article was written by Labanya Prakash Jena and Prasad Ashok Thakur and was first published by the World Economic Forum. https://www.weforum.org/agenda/2024/02/green-hydrogen-global-trade/

A Predictable Global Policy Environment

As far as creating national policies is concerned, only around thirty countries have national strategies for low-carbon hydrogen (including GH2). Only forty-four hydrogen-related policies emerged between 2009–21, typically demonstrated in technical and financial support measures, such as grants, loans or tax concessions. As the GH2 sector grows, these countries will come out with new policies and revamp existing ones; countries who are on the fence to join the GH2 bandwagon will emerge with their own policies. It is crucial these policies are in alignment with the Agreement on Technical Barriers to Trade (TBT) and Agreement on Subsidies and Countervailing Measures (SCM). This will help weave in predictability, coherency and transparency in accordance with WTO frameworks. It can reduce the cross-border value-chain costs associated with the GH2 ecosystem. International institutions can provide policy-related technical assistance to developing countries to bring coherence to the GH2 trade ecosystem.

Harmonised Quality Standards to Promote 'Green' Trade

Policies that simultaneously influence trade and climate are an important manifestation of the interdisciplinary approach taken by national governments. In addition to tariffs, H2 and commodities manufactured using it as a feedstock (ammonia, steel, refinery products, etc.) may attract tax regimes based on their embedded carbon content. The recently introduced EU-Carbon Border Adjustment Mechanism (CBAM) serves as a prominent example. Starting in 2026, GH2/ammonia or steel produced with GH2 may be subject to lower taxes compared to their carbon-intensive variants in the EU. In the USA, four bills were introduced in Congress recently to address issues related to the application of a fee on some imported goods whose carbon intensity exceeds that of the same goods produced in the USA. Other countries are expected to follow suit.

Hence, it is important to promote equity and coherence in national legislation to avoid global value chain disruptions. Accordingly, a recent WTO-IRENA report states that a robust and internationally harmonised 'quality infrastructure' (QI) system can create a design basis for the global development of the GH2 ecosystem. The newly created ISO 19870 can suggest pathways that may be adopted to determine the carbon footprint attributable to the manufacturing, conditioning and transfer of hydrogen to its consumption centres. Trading entities can leverage such QI systems to demonstrate the trustworthiness of their underlying carbon quantification systems. It can also facilitate the work of accredited, independent and competent agencies to verify the carbon footprint of H2 before it gets imported into territories that apply trade-related carbon policies.

Redirect Fossil-fuel Subsidies

To decisively steer towards a net-zero pathway by 2050 for the globe, an average of $136 billion a year is necessary across the hydrogen value chain between 2023 and 2050; the world is looking at a significant investment gap of $790 billion by 2030. To bridge this viability gap and to facilitate an equitable clean energy transition, existing subsidies provided to carbon-intensive fuels like diesel, kerosene, LPG, etc. can be phased out, while being respectful of the needs of less-privileged communities. The resulting savings can be used to reduce/eliminate trade-related barriers on products and services that support faster clean energy adoption to create a level playing field for emerging substitutes like GH2 and its derivatives. The resulting incentives can aim to boost green innovation, e.g., cleantech solutions, development of adaptation measures and market development for green products and services.

International Cooperation in Government Procurement

A progressive and climate-friendly government procurement regime can provide a fillip to the deployment of GH2 and related technologies by creating predictable demand and reducing uptake uncertainty. Here, the WTO's Agreement on Government Procurement, together with other relevant WTO rules, can be used as a reference to ensure open government procurement markets to support GH2 ecosystems. The importance of transparency, dialogue and global cooperation to avoid trade tensions cannot be over-emphasised. Subsidies for local energy transition requirements can entice investment inflows in climate-sensitive infrastructure and technology. At the same time, they can be interpreted as barriers to free global trade. Therefore, incentives should be conceived to strike a balance between economic, social and trade considerations to support a just and equitable transition.

India's Opportunity to Unlock the Clean Energy Potential of North Africa[1]

According to International Renewable Energy Agency (IRENA), clean energy contributes a minuscule 5 per cent of the overall energy generation mix in North African countries compared to the global average of 25 per cent. In Egypt, Algeria, Libya, Morocco, Tunisia and Mauritania, renewables continue to play second fiddle to fossil fuels despite these countries' serious efforts to decarbonise their energy systems. This reality is not commensurate with the virtually limitless clean energy potential offered by the embedded presence of some of the world's most favourable sites for solar and wind energy generation in the region, thanks to sunshine throughout the year and vast coastal plains. The abundant production of clean energy at a lower price can make this region a hydrogen hub for the shipping industry, given its proximity to the high seas of the Atlantic and the Mediterranean.

Leveraging the presence of a virtually limitless supply of seawater, the region can become a net exporter of green hydrogen/ammonia. The brine generated as a rejection of the reverse osmosis process for green hydrogen/ammonia can be used for developing a battery manufacturing ecosystem in the region. Additionally, an entire bouquet of ancillary products and services linked to green hydrogen/chemicals transport, storage and distribution can turbocharge the local economies that have seen long periods of sluggishness due to dormant business sentiments arising out of political instability. India is fast emerging as a clean energy powerhouse. As India is aiming for global leadership in the clean energy sector, North Africa can emerge as a strategic partner.

Green hydrogen to Decarbonise the Shipping Industry

The Suez Canal puts North Africa at the crossroads of global trade. With more than 22,000 ship transits in 2022, the canal is one of the world's most important maritime routes. It accounts for about 12 per cent of the world's trade and about 30 per cent of global container traffic and cargo, valued

[1] The article was written by Labanya Prakash Jena and Prasad Ashok Thakur and was first published by the ET Energy World (From the *Economic Times*). https://energy.economictimes.indiatimes.com/news/renewable/indias-opportunity-to-unlock-the-clean-energy-potential-of-north-africa/98087637?utm_source=linkedin_web&utm_medium=social&utm_campaign=socialsharebuttons

more than USD 1 trillion per annum. Such statistics present enormous opportunities for the region to become the capital of green shipping in the world. Leveraging favourable green hydrogen/ammonia solutions for the shipping industry co-developed with India, the region can play a pivotal role in decarbonising the shipping industry. The recent India-Egypt MoU aimed at setting up green hydrogen facilities with investments of USD 8 billion for a capacity of 20 thousand tonnes annually in the Suez Canal Economic Zone is a promising start. Private sector players like ReNew Power have also expressed interest in the region.

Leveraging Natural Partnership to Overcome Challenges

India is presently hosting G20 with global green growth as its central agenda. India also extended an invitation to Egypt for the G20 Summit scheduled in September 2023 as a special guest, thus elevating its strategic partnership with the region to the next level. Moreover, India and Morocco have recently co-chaired the first India-Arab Energy Forum to promote energy trade and clean technologies. This is in line with the Indian foreign policy of prioritising Africa, highlighted by the fact that more than thirty-two heads of state or government from Africa have visited India in the last four years. Especially when it comes to climate change, India's policy of south-south cooperation with Africa is well-defined and consistent. These facts underscore the harmony India shares with the entire region on critical issues related to climate change. Forging an enduring and consistent clean energy policies in the host countries in North Africa can help manage risks and improve the investor sentiment. As a start, India can quickly increase its diplomatic presence in these nations by opening eighteen new diplomatic missions as planned.

Sharing of Green Energy Capabilities

As its clean energy landscape rapidly evolves, India is increasingly looking to share its successes and experiences on climate action with its international partners. India and North Africa can proactively open avenues for collaborative projects in technology transfer-based exports, project-finance and management, common policy alignment between local governments and exchange of corporates, academics, startups and civil society. Thus, India should aim to create country-specific capabilities in the clean energy sector. Such cross-functional partnerships to create viable business models, green-finance instruments, benign policy frameworks and robust supply chains can help North Africa embark on a path of prosperity and sustainability. Besides, India can offer diversified assistance to North Africa that not only develop the clean energy sector but also create associated local green jobs through skill development and Mass Open Online Courses programmes supported by India. The International Solar Alliance can be leveraged to catalyse such initiatives to promote rapid institutional development in the region. To begin with, India can co-develop country-specific clean energy roadmaps for the North Africa region. This can serve as a blueprint for India to become an active stakeholder in their green development gameplan. In alignment with its domestic clean energy trajectories, India can set a target of installing 30 GW/year capacity in the North African region by 2030.

In the 20th century, India's role in supporting North African countries during their decolonisation efforts was well recognised. As India strives to achieve its own energy independence by 2047 through ambitious clean energy initiatives, it can forge strategic partnerships with North Africa to help them unshackle the chains of fossil fuels.

Pathways to Decarbonise the Cement Sector[1]

Cement is considered a hard-to-decarbonise industry due to its peculiar energy needs and processes; it contributes to about 8–9 per cent of global greenhouse gas (GHG) emissions. In its present form the industry is water intensive and polluting, which takes an adverse toll on the environment. Surprisingly, the Cement Production CO2 Intensity, which signifies the amount of carbon dioxide emitted per unit of cement manufactured, is more in developed countries than in developing countries. A survey conducted in 2015 by Global Efficiency Intelligence, an energy and environmental consulting and market research firm, suggests that Cement Production CO2 Intensity (kgCO2/t cement) in the US and Europe was ~820 kgCO2/t and ~620 kgCO2/t respectively, whereas Cement Production CO2 Intensity in China and India was ~540 kgCO2/t and ~515 kgCO2/t, respectively. Given that cement is essential for erecting infrastructure and for housing, it will continue to be used, particularly in developing countries. It is, therefore, imperative to decarbonise the cement industry to meet the global climate ambition.

The main methods to reduce GHG emission related to energy consumption from the cement industry are heating efficiency, fuel switching and electrification of cement kilns. Carbon Capture Storage (CCS) will also be essential as it is nearly impossible to achieve zero-carbon emissions in cement production. While companies have already taken heating-efficiency measures, the other three methods are at various stages of development. Switching to clean energy depends on its landed cost and availability. The feasibility of adding large-scale CCS is expected to take at least a decade to be commercially feasible. The existing applied technologies can reduce CO2 emissions to a limited extent; however, there is a need to invest heavily in energy-efficient technologies, electrification of cement kilns and CCS to reduce thermal fuel-related emissions from cement.

Reducing CO2 emission from cement production processes depends on the type of mineral and chemical admixtures and changing cement chemistry. The new cement chemistries, alternative materials and new chemical production methods are expected to achieve materiality in commercial

[1] The article was written by Labanya Prakash Jena and Prasad Ashok Thakur and was first published by GITEX IMPACT. https://gitextimpact.com/2023/04/11/pathways-to-decarbonise-the-cement-sector/

deployment but still need further investment in R&D to reduce technology costs and running of pilot projects to demonstrate its commercial viability.

Establishing an Innovation Ecosystem

A McKinsey study suggests that CO2 removal can be achieved in the cement industry through technological innovation and new growth horizons. These technologies may take a long time to substantially reduce carbon emissions without hampering the profitability of cement firms. Balancing these parameters warrants making crucial investments and setting up an innovation pipeline around the cement industry.

Investment in Low-carbon Technologies

The cement industry currently lacks solid incentives to invest in low-carbon technologies due to the absence of a carbon pricing mechanism and limited regulatory pressure. The repurposing of existing manufacturing facilities with the goal of reducing carbon emissions needs additional investment. Raising new equity capital can reduce the return on equity (ROE) and dilute the stake of existing shareholders—both financial decisions are not in the best interest of existing shareholders. Financing through debt capital can be ideal for keeping ROE intact but may face debt capital access challenges. Debt capital providers may not be convinced of the additional cash flow ability to repurpose existing manufacturing facilities. Once integrated with the plant, it will be difficult to separate the new technologies and ring-fence the asset for collateralisation. The existing regulations on the cement industry is not able to exert pressure on the cement industry to invest heavily in low-carbon technologies.

The Role of Transition Financing

Concessional transition financing can help cement companies to reduce the existing plant's carbon intensity. Cement companies in developing countries can get support from Multilateral Development Banks (MDBs) and International Climate Finance institutions such as the Green Climate Fund with a mandate to invest in low-carbon technologies that can provide concessional debt financing for cement plants that have a concrete plan to reduce carbon emissions.

In developed countries, governments can offer concession debt capital to help cement companies with a concrete green transition plan. Since the carbon intensity of the cement industry in developed countries is high compared to developing countries, governments can levy a tax based on their Cement Production CO2 Intensity. The money generated from this can be used for a research fund to invest in low-carbon cement technologies. Corporates can also raise capital from banks and financial institutions through the issuance of transition bonds or loans. The duration of loans or bonds must be long enough to deploy low-carbon technologies today but incentivise the company to generate financial savings in the long run. For example, an increase in carbon prices in the future can help those companies that have already deployed low-carbon technologies.

Transition financing, loans or bonds (at a corporate level) are better options as the financier can assess the transition of the company across plants and not just a specific one. Transition financing can set carbon intensity targets for the company. It can add carbon-emission-related covenants to the loan/bond contract to incentivise the company to invest in less carbon-intensive technologies.

The Rewards of Collaboration

The collaboration between cement companies is critical where they can voluntarily pledge to share a percentage of their profit. The proceeds from these voluntary contributions can be pooled together to strategically invest, through an open, transparent and competitive process, in relevant start-ups/incubators and to promote outcome-oriented projects in low-carbon technologies pertaining to the sector. The bigger contribution to the financial pool as a share of the company profits, the faster the sector can leapfrog towards achieving net-zero while simultaneously reaping the benefits of economies of scale.

Decarbonising Cement Sector: Need to Bind Technology Innovation with Transition Finance[1]

To achieve its net-zero targets, it is imperative for India to seize all possible low-carbon pathways across the sectors and functions. Cement is considered one of the hard-to-decarbonise industries due to its peculiar energy needs and processes. It is estimated that the global cement industry contributes to about 8–9 per cent of GHG emissions, 2–3 per cent of its energy demand and about 9 per cent of its industrial water withdrawals. Further, the selection of fuels for cement kilns, and in part the kiln materials currently used, lead to notable air pollutant emissions. The cement industry alone is responsible for about 8 per cent of the total national emissions in India. Cement remains integral to the country's industrial, infrastructural and housing growth story. The government and businesses must jointly summon their innovative capabilities to significantly and expeditiously reduce the carbon footprint of this versatile sector.

Technology Choice

Cement manufacturing releases CO2 through two main activities: energy use and calcination reactions. Energy-related emissions (30–40 per cent of direct CO2 emissions) occur when thermal fuels, most commonly coal, are used to heat a pre-calciner and rotary kiln. The other primary source of direct CO2 emissions is 'process emissions' which come from a chemical reaction in the pre-calciner. India's cement industry's carbon intensity is better than the global average, 3.1 GJ/tonne of clinker and 80 kWh/tonne of cement, vs. the global average of 3.5 GJ/tonne of clinker and 91 kWh/tonne of cement. Still, this is higher than its peers in Europe and the United States.

The main options to reduce carbon intensity in the cement industry are improving the thermal efficiency of cement-making equipment, fuel switching, electrification of cement kilns and carbon capture and

[1] The article was written by Labanya Prakash Jena and Prasad Ashok Thakur and was first published by the ET Energy World (From the *Economic Times*). https://energy.economictimes.indiatimes.com/news/power/decarbonizing-cement-sector-need-to-bind-technology-innovation-with-transition-finance/97587405?utm_source=linkedin_web&utm_medium=social&utm_campaign=socialsharebuttons

sequestration (CCS). While thermal efficiency measures have already largely been implemented, the other three methods are at various stages of development and usage. Fuel switching depends on the price and availability of zero-carbon electricity and the feasibility of carbon capture and storage at the plant site. While zero-carbon electricity price has significantly reduced, CCS will take a longer time, ten to fifteen years, to be commercially feasible. In process emission, mineral and chemical admixtures and the changing composition of cement chemistry and materials, are critical mechanisms for reducing CO2 emissions.

Investment Boost for R&D

A McKinsey study suggests that CO2 emissions from cement could be reduced by 75 per cent by 2050. However, operational advances may contribute only about 20 per cent of this decarbonisation effort. The remainder is expected to come from technological innovation and new growth horizons. It implies that cement industries need to look beyond the horizon and invest heavily in new cement chemistries and other carbon-efficient technologies. A few new technologies are encountering success through pilot stages and transitioning into being implemented on a smaller scale. However, it is well recognised that such technologies may take a while to deliver the desired benefits at scale. Hence, the case to make crucial investments for establishing an innovation ecosystem around the product becomes stronger and more urgent.

Addressing Systemic Market Challenges

The cement industry lacks compelling incentives to invest in CO2-mitigating due to the absence of functional carbon markets. Despite pressure from civil society, green investors and financial regulators, largely based inside and outside India, the pace of change is lackadaisical. To reduce the carbon intensity of existing plants, the industry should aim to repurpose existing manufacturing facilities through efficiency measures in the consumption of energy, raw materials and catalysts. Raising debt capital to reduce carbon intensity will be challenging for the industry due to the lack of credible historical datasets on the energy efficiency of the novel process changes and the perceived risk of replaced equipment not yielding adequate financial savings to manufacturing plants. Besides, once integrated with the project facility, it is difficult for the lender to separate and ring-fence the asset for collateralisation. Reducing carbon costs is much higher than the presently existing penalty structure (read carbon price). Due to the highly intertwined nature of the cement prices and infrastructure financing models in the country, the government may not impose a high carbon price on such an important sector as it may derail its economic growth plans in the post-pandemic and war-impacted global economy.

Solutions for a Seamless Transition

Transition financing can help companies reduce the carbon intensity of existing plants. In the case of capital-intensive technologies, the companies can raise debt capital from commercial banks, Multilateral Development Banks and similar development finance institutions. Such transition financing (at a corporate level) may be a better option as the financer can assess the transition across the company's cement plants and not a specific cement plant. Transition financing can set carbon intensity targets for individual cement companies. It can add a carbon- emission-related covenant to the loan/bond (in the case of transition financing) to incentivise the companies to adopt a less carbon-intensive business trajectory. The company can adopt and adhere to carbon emission reduction targets for the short, medium and long-term horizons.

Clean Cement Cess (CCC)

Putting a carbon price on fuel consumption or emissions creates an incentive for the most efficient plants to fully use their capacity and, at the same time, restrains the use of the most inefficient ones. Like a coal cess, the government can put a price on carbon emissions from the cement industries. The collected cess (CCC) can be used to stimulate an R&D ecosystem that can exclusively focus on pathbreaking research in low-carbon cement technologies, efficient financial models and responsive policy frameworks relevant to the industry. The benefits of such an interdisciplinary approach will be shared with all organisations related to this sector. A well-structured CCC has multiple advantages. The bigger the financial pool of CCC, the faster the sector can accelerate toward the development of low-carbon cement technologies. A price on carbon emissions creates an incentive for the most efficient cement plants to fully use their capacity while at the same time restraining the use of the most inefficient ones.

It is a well-known fact that the progress of a developing country like India is intricately linked with its ability to offer state-of-the-art infrastructure. With India's ambitious Net-Zero 2070 target acting as a guiding light, the time has come for the cement sector to make its rightful contributions to it. The sector must quickly evolve from a mere product supplier to a much larger role of a construction solutions provider.

Reimagining India's Long Duration Energy Storage Gameplan[1]

The ever-increasing share of clean energy in India's power mix requires astute management of supply and demand, transmission flow patterns and overall energy system stability. Long duration energy storage (LDES) is best positioned to provide a solution to these issues to create an affordable, dependable, net-zero grid. The US Department of Energy (DOE) defines systems that can store energy for more than 10 hours at a time as LDES. It can act as a strategic energy reservoir for India's energy security. India is expected to commission 30–50 GW LDES to achieve its 2030 target of deploying 500 GW of non-fossil fuel-based energy.

This target will entail receiving dynamic support from India's policy and regulatory environment. By 2030, the US DOE's Energy Earth-shot Initiative aims to reduce the cost of grid-scale LDES by 90 per cent. By then, the global LDES market is expected to grow fifteen-fold, as per Bloomberg New Energy Finance, which translates to a global addition of about 390 GW capacity to reach 410 GW—a huge opportunity for India to grab on the exports front. India needs to refresh its strategies elaborated in the 'Energy Storage Mission' and the 'Energy Storage System Roadmap for India: 2019–2032' to realise its bold new vision.

India: Policy and Planning for Evolving Landscapes

India has set ambitious targets for renewable energy; however, there is no clearly articulated target for LDES. The country needs an integrated energy policy to support emerging LDES technologies and promote their adoption in diverse scenarios. To arrive at these targets, it should holistically explore services LDES can provide across sectors and applications like electricity generation, industry, household, commercial, etc. The 'National Mission on Transformative Mobility and Battery Storage' attempts to cursorily allude to LDES, but primarily from the mobility lens. A policy target for multi-sectoral applications can provide a direction for markets, talent and capital. A policy for LDES purchase obligations can also be considered during the initial stages to create a market and accelerate investment.

---

[1] The article was written by Labanya Prakash Jena and Prasad Ashok Thakur and was first published by the ETBFSI (From the *Economic Times*). https://bfsi.economictimes.indiatimes.com/blog/reimagining-indias-long-duration-energy-storage-gameplan/96117684

To help stakeholders make informed decisions, Government of India (GoI) can create a central repository for LDES knowledge on various technologies, performance characteristics, application scenarios, standards and financial models. GoI can use diverse platforms to disseminate these learnings. Such a knowledge-based foundation can provide a head-start to the domestic industry, startups, policymakers, regulators and financers. Networks of public and private research organisations can create open-source tools to shine a light on the performance of various emerging LDES technologies and associated value streams. This can contribute towards developing a level playing field for all players. It can also trigger the co-evolution of supplementary capabilities and synergy in energy distribution systems, cybersecurity of the grid, and demand-side management. Additionally, a cost-competitive, sustainable and giga-scale LDES battery manufacturing ecosystem needs reliable supplies of raw materials. GoI can leverage its diplomatic capital to create supply chains that are secure and resilient against geopolitical risks. It must ensure raw materials are available from domestic and international sources without environmental challenges and social conflicts.

Financial Support

The uptake of LDES technologies can be supported through financial schemes and incentives from the public sector. Typical risks emanating from new-technology performance, adoption of evolving standards and market and policy dynamics can be capped by preparing response scenarios in advance. Financial support can be in the form of tax breaks, electricity subsidies, land leases at industry-friendly terms, higher capital subsidies, easy access to foreign investments, stamp-duty subsidies and R&D grants. Simultaneously, investments in programme management capabilities can be made to support digital and multi-modal supply chains, the protection of IP rights and the creation of robust compliance frameworks.

Creating a Talent Pipeline

By leveraging the incentives and infrastructure offered by initiatives like 'Atmanirbhar Bharat', 'Make in India' and 'Skill India', a talent pipeline in LDES can be created. For India to emerge as a leader in this highly specialised sector, this is a crucial action-item. A modular two-to-four-years curriculum can be introduced for skilling of new and existing workforce. To remain in tune with global developments, international partnerships and certification programmes can be launched. GoI can offer MOOC training and workshops on LDES for Least Developed Countries and Small Island Developing States to create local green jobs. Equipped with multi-disciplinary knowledge in design, R&D, manufacturing 4.0, logistics, operations and business management, this talent pool can be an asset to the world. As more indigenously manufactured LDES capacity gets deployed in India and abroad, more use cases will create the demand for ancillary services. As this body of knowledge and practice grows, the ability of an India-trained workforce to customise and calibrate solutions for customer-centric applications will be honed and appreciated.

Seizing Future Opportunities

The global demand for LDES to support its green energy transition targets should be leveraged by India. It can emerge as a partner of choice to other countries through the creation of ambitious giga-scale manufacturing capabilities along with the introduction of energy-as-a-service offerings. Here, a public-private partnership body to coordinate and integrate union and state policies, private sector programmes, academic contributions and startup initiatives can work wonders. It can reduce friction between various stakeholders, eliminate redundancy and mitigate the adverse impacts of market upheavals. It can also facilitate the recycling, reuse and planet-friendly disposal of materials used in LDES. This can reduce India's import dependency and pave the way for embarking on a faster, sustainable and inclusive trajectory towards net-zero.

Blue Carbon: India's Time to Create Some Waves[1]

India's commitment to its 2070 net-zero target entails that it must explore all potential interventions and leverage them to their fullest. Here, nature-based solutions like blue carbon ecosystems e.g., mangroves, tidal and salt marshes, seagrasses, etc., can be crucial for carbon sequestration. However, India's 'Long-Term Low-Carbon Development Strategy' document submitted to the United Nations Framework Convention on Climate Change (UNFCCC) is not focusing on this opportunity. The absence of a clear pathway for the restoration of blue carbon storage assets can be a major source of carbon emissions in the future.

[1] The article was written by Labanya Prakash Jena and Prasad Ashok Thakur and was first published by the Observer Research Foundation. https://www.orfonline.org/expert-speak/blue-carbon-indias-time-to-create-some-waves

Climate change Mitigation and Adaptation Benefits

India is blessed with a 7,500+ kilometre-long coastline. As per Anirban Akhand et al. (2022), India could presently have about 5,000 sq. km of mangroves, 500 sq. km of seagrasses and anywhere between 300 to 1,400 sq. km of salt marshes which cumulatively adds up to about 0.5 per cent of the country's total area. Despite their small expanse, these coastal systems can sequester carbon considerably faster and for millions of years. According to Hamilton and Friess (2018), they can capture carbon dioxide (CO_2) up to twenty times greater than any other terrestrial ecosystem, including boreal and tropical forests. Presently, their total carbon sequestration potential has been estimated as 702.42 million tonnes of CO_2e or about 22 per cent of India's annual carbon emission. It has also been estimated that there is an additional sequestration potential of 207.91 million tonnes of CO_2e if the mangrove cover is conserved and protected.

Additionally, coastal ecosystems provide climate adaptation benefits such as protection from hurricanes and sea-level rise, prevention of shoreline erosion and regulation of coastal water quality. Moreover, restoring coastal areas offer several ecosystem services such as food security, livelihoods (small-scale fisheries) and biodiversity. Unfortunately, coastal ecosystems are eroding due to urbanisation, the conversion of land into agriculture and aquaculture and extreme weather events. The 'Nature' journal mentions India as a 'blue carbon wealth recipient country' instead of a blue carbon 'donor' country. This suggests an underutilisation of blue carbon resources in India.

India Needs to Give Impetus to Blue Carbon

The lack of focus on blue carbon in its low-carbon strategy implies India must bring about a 'sea change' in its understanding of its coastal ecosystems as a strategic carbon sequestration reserve. Saying that India has turned a blind eye toward these possibilities is not an overstatement. It may so happen that some of India's previous activities under its afforestation and reforestation initiatives include minor aspects of the restoration and rejuvenation of coastal ecosystems. However, with changing times it is imperative to earmark and unify such projects under the broader umbrella of 'blue carbon' to keep up with the evolving nature of global climate policy.

Time for a National Institute for Blue Carbon

The Government of India should realise that the country has so far relied only on homogenous literature on blue carbon, often by very few subject matter experts. It should now step in to create, compile and formalise these databases towards institutionalising this workstream.

To help itself emerge as a leader in the blue-carbon sector, India must draw inspiration from specialised peer organisations like the National Institute of Wind Energy (NIWE), National Institute of Solar Energy (NISE), National Institute of Bioenergy (NIBE), etc., and set up an organisation for the blue-carbon sector. This new institute can collaborate closely with the Indian Meteorological Department, National Institute of Oceanography, National Botanical Research Institute, ISRO, IIT Bombay's National Centre of Excellence in Carbon Capture and Utilisation, etc., to fulfil the necessary conditions needed to catalyse this sector. It can promote the establishment of requisite standards, codes and peer-review frameworks for assessing blue carbon solutions. It can also harbour human resource skilling activities, incubate startups and promote innovation clusters that prevent the degradation of coastal ecosystems, retain soil nutrition and conserve indigenous biodiversity while respecting the cultures and aspirations of local communities.

National Mission for Blue Carbon

To streamline the technological developments with financial and policy interventions in the blue-carbon sector, it is important that the GoI launches a strategic mission for the same. It can decide national targets for relevant sectors that contribute towards the development of a blue-carbon ecosystem and subsequently define the phase-wise strategies for value-chain development for acquiring knowledge, manpower, money and materials that can stimulate the country's collective efforts. It can identify the potential demand generation actions like blue carbon obligations while pushing to put in place the key enablers for domestic and international players in this space. Setting up a robust carbon market in the country can be a critical element of this journey. It can launch pilot projects with the private sector/NGOs/Think Tanks while ensuring appropriate monitoring, compliance and risk-mitigation guidelines. According to a McKinsey report, blue carbon nature-based systems like peatland restoration can be achieved at a price of US$50/tCO2 equivalent by the year 2050 in India. It also proposes that emerging blue-carbon solutions can compete with nature-based solutions of land. The proposed mission can be empirically validated through pilots and decide financial outlays for the short-to-medium terms to outperform market expectations. Subsequently, the experience can be shared globally.

International Partnerships

Due to its geostrategic location, India can be a leading beacon to synchronise cross-functional and cross-continental efforts in the blue carbon space. It can forge meaningful consensus across bilateral and multilateral forums. Also, for its own interests, it must actively participate in platforms like the Blue Carbon Initiative, International Partnership for Blue Carbon and various upcoming projects related to nurturing blue forests in the Indian Ocean. India's recent support of the French-led 'High Ambition Coalition on Biodiversity Beyond National Jurisdiction' and its participation in the 'One Ocean Summit' are early steps in the right direction. India can also support Small Island Developing States (SIDS) on their vast blue carbon resources. The lack of India's thought leadership on this front has led to disappointment amongst such countries in the climate dialogues. As India has recently taken over the presidency of the G20, it can summon its capabilities to fill in this void. The water bodies surrounding India have deeply influenced its civilisational evolution. Its ancient ethos, literature and manuscripts have always venerated the gifts received from the high seas. India's ambitions to emerge as a climate leader warrants its rise as a leader in the blue-carbon arena.

Scaling Circular Economy[1]

The adverse impact of a linear economy, where products are manufactured, consumed and discarded, is evident in the environment and health of humans and animals in India. If we continue with a linear economic model, the problem will only worsen due to a rising material demand in a growing economy and product demand due to a large consumer base.

Circular economy (CE) can alleviate these challenges by reducing discarded products in multiple ways, including prolonging the life of products through proper maintenance and repair, changing product ownership in the secondary market, refurbishing and recycling.

Reducing Pollution through Circular Economy

India's commitment to achieving net-zero by 2070 needs a myriad of technologies, policy, regulatory reforms and innovative financial and business models. CE is one of the models that can support India's ambition to reach net-zero through energy savings. According to a research paper, the CE has the potential to save 6–11 per cent of worldwide energy consumption. In addition, India's path to a developed and green economy needs an enormous volume of materials, most of which would be imported. Reorienting from a linear to a CE will reduce demand for imported materials, thereby making it self-sufficient and saving foreign exchange.

Although there are several benefits of a CE, there are challenges to adopting it on a large scale. The key challenges are the difficulty and cost of collecting used products, the lack of a supply chain infrastructure to reverse product flows and limited public participation; recovery value may be less than the cost; extremely heavy products are difficult to transport and recycle and lack of existence of a secondary market.

Solutions

A contractual model targeting products that use extensive steel, aluminium and cement can be an impactful and implementable solution that can address the challenges mentioned above. These products are energy intensive, hard to decarbonise and polluting, so recycling products using these materials will

[1] The article was written by Labanya Prakash Jena and Chinmaya Behera and was first published by the Observer Research Foundation. https://www.orfonline.org/expert-speak/scaling-circular-economy

reduce energy needs and mitigate pollution problems. Technically, they can be refurbished and reused.

The contractual model stipulates that assets must be returned to the manufacturer after the end of asset life. For example, a steel company enters a contract with an auto manufacturer or auto component manufacturer. The condition is that the steel is no longer recycled or refurbished and must be returned to the steel manufacturer. The ownership doesn't rest with the consumers after using the product if the consumers are not refurbishing or recycling themselves. The contract period can be the life of the asset. However, the user will pay the usual price of the product to the manufacturer upfront, not lease payments over the lease period in a leasing contract. There can be flexible upgrade options where consumers can switch to newer, more efficient models, encouraging continuous improvement in sustainability.

Maintenance Rests with the User

In this contractual model, the user is responsible for regular maintenance to ensure products remain in optimal condition, reducing the need for replacements and, thus, waste. Maintenance practices must adhere to eco-friendly standards (e.g., using biodegradable lubricants). The manufacturing company trains users on the optimal use of the product to maximise its lifespan and efficiency. They can provide ongoing support to ensure users can address any operational issues without resorting to replacements. The manufacturer can offer incentives or discounts to consumers for maintaining the products well and returning them in good condition. A third party can be appointed where regular audits can ensure compliance with the sustainability goals set in the contract. This structure encourages the reuse, refurbishment and proper disposal of products, ensuring a significant reduction in waste and an increase in resource efficiency across the product lifecycle.

Favourable Policies and Regulations to Enhance Effectiveness

India has an extended producers' responsibility policy but is limited to plastic waste management. To make the model impactful, policymakers must extend its scope and encompass a broader range of materials and products. The first step should be to identify products that offer substantial environmental benefits (for example, reducing energy needs compared to the linear model) that can be refurbished or recycled without incurring significant additional costs. The regulator can make it compulsory for the manufacturers of the identified products to enter into a contractual agreement with the user, in which the products must be returned to the manufacturer in case they are not refurbished and reused. The government can offer tax benefits and incentives if certain thresholds are crossed. For example, if the manufacturers recycle or refuse more than 60 per cent of new product sales, they can assume 2 per cent of tax benefits in their income tax.

Besides, the government must support building infrastructure to collect used products from end consumers for refurbishing or recycling. Regulators can make it compulsory to disassemble products where high-value products can be reused (e.g., electronic items in batteries). The government can establish a green arbitration panel specialising in environmental conflicts to resolve disputes. The use of mediation and arbitration is needed before any legal action to maintain partnership ethos and sustainability focus.

The manufacturer gains a reputation as a sustainable corporation and they disclose better recycling rates compared to their peers. The consumer reduces operational costs through efficient and well-maintained products.

Peatland Restoration is Crucial but How do We Pay for It?[1]

Peatlands, called moors, mires or bogs, are terrestrial wetland ecosystems formed from partially decomposed carbon-rich organic matter. Peatlands cover about 3 per cent of the surface of the earth and create the largest natural terrestrial carbon store, maintaining a constant amount of carbon. Aside from minimising flood risk, conserving biodiversity, preserving air quality and purifying the water table, peatlands sequester approximately 4 gigatonnes of CO2 per year, more than all other vegetation types in the world combined. Preserving peatlands can help achieve global net-zero ambition and benefits climate adaptation.

Exploitative land use practices, large-scale artificial drainage and underestimation of ecosystem services have made peatlands vulnerable to irreversible degradation. As a result, we face an ever-increasing risk of tipping the global peatland greenhouse gas (GHG) balance from a carbon sink—absorbing more carbon than it releases—to a carbon source—releasing more carbon than it absorbs. It has been calculated that the global CO2 emissions from drained peatlands have increased by 20 per cent between 1990 and 2008 and now roughly account for 5 per cent of all anthropogenic emissions.

A meta-study conducted by the International Union for Conservation of Nature and the University of Oxford reveals that most countries need to explicitly include actions related to peatlands or wetlands in their nationally determined contributions. So, governments need to invest the required capital for peatland restoration. Capital must flow for the restoration of peatland; devoid of timely action, the bill is likely to get bulkier.

Capital Intensive Peatland Restoration

The costs of a restoration project primarily include capital outlays associated with rewetting, replanting, brash cutting and sphagnum plugging, amongst other restoration techniques. These restoration costs account for over 85 per cent of the total costs related to the project. Being a capital-intensive business, it needs long-term capital at a reasonable cost.

---

[1] The article was written by Labanya Prakash Jena and Jolly Sinha and was first published by the World Economic Forum. https://www.weforum.org/agenda/2023/02/peatland-restoration-is-crucial-but-how-do-we-pay-for-it/

Public finance is unlikely to provide sufficient additional funds. In the United Kingdom, the government promised £10 million through its natural environment impact fund toward the restoration of 35,000 hectares of wetland, which represents 1 per cent of all the modified to actively degraded peatlands in the country. However, public finance can be key in establishing institutions and mechanisms to attract private capital.

There is a need for more revenue-generating, self-sustaining financing mechanisms which provide a lucrative opportunity for private capital providers to participate in the peatland restoration business. We propose setting up a natural capital financing facility that blends public and private capital. The facility pools capital from various sources and offers upfront, low-cost and long-duration capital to aggregators to cover capital and operating expenses for the peatlands restoration programme.

Public financiers provide crucial capital grants to finance a significant portion of upfront restoration costs, while private investors cover the residual part of capital costs. Public capital with a mandate to generate public capital can provide non-returnable grant capital, enabling private investors to generate a required return from their investment.

The private capital providers would be the class of investors having long-term investment horizons with an appetite for taking illiquidity risks, such as pension funds and insurance companies. The owner of peatlands, mostly public authorities, transfers the usage rights to the financing facility for a certain year, enabling the facility to recover capital through monetising the services of the peatland.

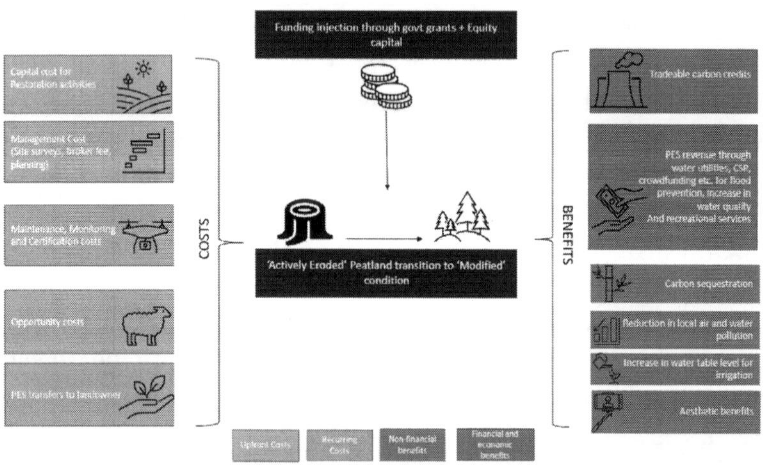

Costs and benefits of peatland restoration

Source: Prepare by Labanya Prakash Jena

Recovering Cost of Restoration

The financing facility can appoint a project developer responsible for assessing the peatland's condition (near natural to actively eroded) and restoring and maintaining the peatland. The developer will collect a management fee from the financing facility for the restoration and maintenance services of the peatland. The financing facility can hire a third party to provide quality assurance certification that can increase the marketability and price of the ecosystem services.

The primary financial benefit is derived from selling tradable carbon emissions from carbon sequestration (capturing, removal and storage of CO2 from earth's atmosphere) from peatland restoration. There can be a long-term contract between buyer and seller to purchase emission credits at a predetermined price to mitigate carbon pricing volatility. As the carbon price is expected to increase in the future, this source of revenue will be key for the commercial viability of peatland restoration. Besides generating revenue from the sale of carbon credit, there will be a series of payments for a guaranteed flow of ecosystem services (PES). In most cases, the PES is derived from water purification, flood protection and recreational benefits.

Water quality-related benefits derived from peatland restoration can be categorised into two broad categories: 1) reduced drinking water treatment costs and 2) benefits associated with the good ecological condition of water bodies. The water authorities can pay for the water purification benefits. A long water purchase agreement between the water authority and developers can reduce cash flow uncertainty. Often, upland peatlands' contribution to storing water decreases the likelihood of flooding downstream. The local authorities or federal government can pay a portion of the peatland restoration cost as they would invest less for flood protection. Besides, general insurance companies can also cover a part of the restoration cost as insurance claims on assets vulnerable to flood in that area are less likely.

Grazing can be carried out on some of the restoration wetlands—a commercially-priced agreement with local farmers that can generate additional revenue. In addition, peatland can offer recreation services drawing large numbers of tourists; these services can be priced by selling tickets to tourists. Similarly, additional revenue can be generated from outdoor advertising on the peatland. The payments received from the above sources will be used to pay back private financiers, while the multiple revenue sources can mitigate the credit risk of investors. Besides, a long-term contract with carbon credit buyers, water bodies and government authorities can improve the revenue predictability of the project, thereby mitigating risk for private financiers.

Beefing up Cybersecurity for India's Energy Transition[1]

With about 179 GW of installed renewable energy capacity as of July 2023 (40 per cent of total energy capacity), India's electricity grid is fundamentally transforming its character. The transformation of the energy system aligns with the country's ambition of installing 500 GW of non-fossil fuel-based energy capacity by 2030 and achieving its energy independence by 2047. Power sector players are expected to increasingly embrace an army of smart grid-interfacing devices during power generation, transmission, distribution and consumption. On the demand side, popular examples of appliances for home/office/industry and commercial spaces include smart devices for lighting, heating, ventilation and air conditioning (HVAC), cleaning, cooking, etc. Due to their rapid electrification, the mobility and agriculture sectors are also getting intertwined with the power sector. As time progresses, all these smart devices are expected to become increasingly capable of communicating and coordinating with each other and the national grid in real time. One must remember that these energy management use cases are critical in our fight against climate change. However, as the electricity value chain assumes these new characteristics, it will be crucial to ensure that progressive cybersecurity measures are infused into new devices, systems and power infrastructure. Cybersecurity elements should become a non-separable design feature of these systems. The media reports of Chinese hackers targeting seven Indian power hubs, cyberattacks on the United States (US)'s electrical grid emanating from a West-Asian country, cyber warfare between Russia and Ukraine and other such attempts mandate that this threat must be addressed with alacrity.

National Security Concerns

Clean energy generation facilities can exchange significant amounts of data with utility operators and aggregators through a 'smart grid-interactive inverter'. This is a cyber-physical device. Because of its unique functionality, it may pose a risk of cyberattack and may render the national grid operations

[1] The article was written by Labanya Prakash Jena and Prasad Ashok Thakur and was first published by the Observer Research Foundation. https://www.orfonline.org/expert-speak/beefing-up-cybersecurity-for-india-s-energy-transition

insecure. Attackers can exploit this vulnerable intrusion vector to enter the national network and carry out lateral movement to other sensitive and strategically important assets. This is also true for smart grid-interfacing devices in the transmission, distribution and point-of-use value chains. It is well-known that original equipment manufacturers (OEMs) operating outside India possess the capability to manage the operations of these devices remotely. This attribute can be exploited to jeopardise the safety and security of India's national power grid by India's adversaries (state and non-state actors). There is also a perpetually looming threat of strategic databases being breached, as some of them may be surreptitiously maintained/controlled from outside India.

Existing Cybersecurity Framework in India

Cyber Security in Power Sector Guidelines (2021) under the Central Electricity Authority (CEA) incorporate the cardinal principles of cybersecurity for the power sector. These require mandatory compliance by all responsible entities (including renewable energy generation utilities and aggregators). With a multifold increase in the complexity and frequency of cyber threats, this framework should evolve as per the changing requirements of domains like cyber policy, risk assessment and mitigation plans, Chief Information Security Officers (CISO) training, supply chain risks management, incident/sabotage reporting and response actions, cybersecurity audits, etc. The Ministry of Power also created six sectoral Computer Emergency Response Teams (CERT) for thermal, hydro, transmission, grid operations, renewables and distribution. In line with the National Cyber Security Policy, all power sector utilities are expected to board the Cyber Swachhta Kendra (Botnet Cleaning and Malware Analysis Centres). Moreover, an Information Sharing and Analysis Centre (ISAC-Power) was established to provide a common platform for the six CERTs for information sharing and act as a central data repository. Additionally, the National Critical Information Infrastructure Protection Centre (NCIIPC), under the aegis of the National Technical Research Organisation (NTRO), performs the multifaceted role of executing all necessary actions to protect relevant critical infrastructure from untoward incidents in alignment with the Information Technology Act 2000 (amended in 2008). NCIIPC facilitates coherent interventions from stakeholders and increases awareness amongst them about the evolving nature of cyber threats.

Way Forward to Neutralise Power Sector Cybersecurity Threats

Technical initiatives: Through the Grid Controller of India Limited, it is desirable to scrutinise the source code, intellectual property rights and periodic updates of OEMs to their products/software and certify them as ready for interfacing with the national grid. To keep up with the developments in artificial intelligence and machine learning, suitable vulnerability management tools and cyber-attack resilient capabilities may be co-developed with indigenous centres of excellence.

Regulatory initiatives: The CEA and the Ministry of Electronics and Information Technology (MeitY) should work closely with software and hardware manufacturers of foreign origin to build early consensus on complying with the law of the land in letter and spirit. Organisations like the National Institute of Solar Energy, the National Institute of Wind Energy, the National Institute of Bioenergy, etc., must be directed to periodically create an approved list of models and manufacturers for their domains as per the protocol laid down by the CEA and MeitY. It must be made mandatory for equipment suppliers and software developers for clean energy applications to set up their server rooms, data centres, critical R&D centres, design studios and similar critical facilities within the country. Necessary and sufficient firewalls with access controls and IP-based communication protocols must be audited periodically as per global best practices. It must be mandatory for all utilities to nominate a CISO who will reside in India to comply with the country's cybersecurity requirements punctually.

Financial initiatives: To ensure the long-term sustainability and growth of the above efforts, a dedicated budgetary provision can be made within the relevant ministry and a separate power sector cyber security cell must be created. Special financial incentives can be carved out within the production-linked incentives (PLI) for entities creating novel indigenous solutions addressing this issue. Research grants can be extended to support the development of cutting-edge cybersecurity technologies on a mission-mode basis. In the strategic national interest of the country, the government, the private sector, academia and startups must work collectively to develop and manufacture all critical components and associated cyber architecture in India. This will help create a world-class clean energy ecosystem that is safe, reliable and cost-competitive.

Repurposing India's Coal Power Plants: Sustainability-linked Green Bonds as a Financing Solution[1]

India faces a dilemma—balancing its growing energy needs with its pledge to reduce greenhouse gas (GHG) emissions as part of its revised Nationally Determined Contributions (NDC) goals (45 per cent lower GHG emissions compared to 2005 levels by 2030). The early retirement of coal power plants is necessary to meet this target; however, the timing of these retirements is a point of contention amongst policymakers, plant owners, financiers and other stakeholders.

India has pushed back on the US and Germany—leading the Just Energy Transition Partnership (JETP) negotiations—regarding including an early coal phase-out in the discussions. Instead, India has demanded that the JETP financing deal include renewable energy, technology transfer and green jobs without discussing early coal retirement due to its increasing energy demands and socio-political sensitivity. This impasse on receiving global public finance for early coal retirement and just transition leads to the question of how India can meet its emission reduction targets while meeting its rising energy demand.

A Case for Capital Market-based Solutions

In light of this, private utility players (accounting for 35 per cent of India's total coal capacity, around 73 gigawatts (GW)) committed to decarbonising could consider capital market-based solutions to repurpose technically feasible coal power plants into renewables while ensuring a just transition. A study by Climate Risk Horizon estimated that the financial benefits of repurposing coal plants in Maharashtra would outweigh the cost of early retirement by two to four times. Furthermore, it will help the Maharashtra State Electricity Distribution Co save Rs 750 billion (US$9.08 billion) over 10 years due to lower renewable energy power costs. The cost savings will also cover 30–170 per cent of the new capital expenditure required to repurpose

[1] The article was written by Labanya Prakash Jena and Saurabh Trivedi and was first published by the World Economic Forum. https://www.weforum.org/agenda/2023/03/15c15899-5991-4166-92fa-7690581d50c3/

the coal plants into renewable energy plants. This would be a mutually beneficial outcome for coal power producers and off-takers.

Sustainability-linked green bonds

Using sustainability-linked green bonds (SLGBs) could be a possible option to finance the repurposing and just transition of coal power plants into renewable energy plants.

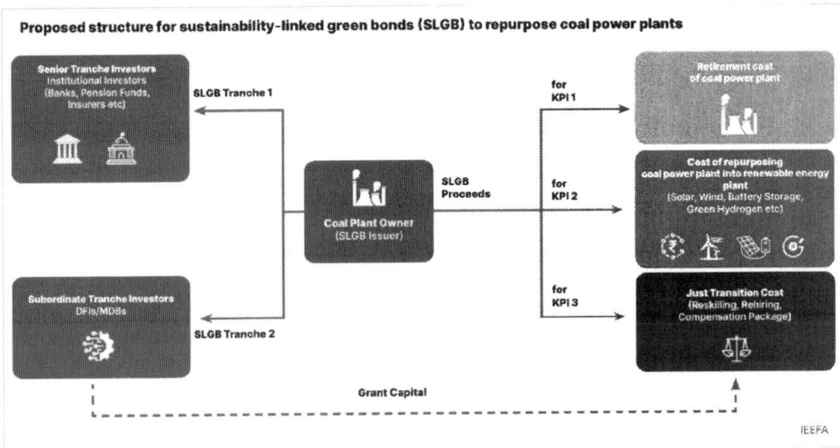

The proposed structure would suit private-sector coal power utilities. These companies, like Tata Power, have more latitude to retire coal plants earlier, have committed to decarbonising and have a strong balance sheet and ability to access debt capital markets. Although state-owned companies can also use this structure, they may be hesitant due to the government's plan to avoid retiring any coal plants before 2030.

SLGB Structure with Potential to Deliver on Decarbonisation and Just Transition

A vanilla sustainability-linked bond (SLB) is structured around key performance indicators (KPIs). These KPIs relate to the issuer's environmental, social and governance targets. Failure to meet these KPI targets usually results in monetary penalties, while reaching them can lead to lower subsequent coupon payments. The SLB market has grown globally to US$244 billion, as of 27 February 2023, since the first issuance in 2019. However, proceeds of vanilla SLBs can end up funding non-green projects, thus raising concerns about greenwashing. Hence, we propose an SLGB structure where the KPIs and the proceeds are tied to specified projects.

Under this proposal, a coal power producer would issue an SLGB with three KPIs:

- Decommissioning coal generation capacity by an ambitious date.
- Adding renewable energy generation capacity prior to or in tandem with coal decommissioning.
- Reskilling, rehiring and compensation package ensuring a just transition from a coal to renewable energy power plant.

The issuer must also ring-fence proceeds of the SLGB to specified projects that would fulfil each KPI to ensure the transparency of the issuance and prevent the misuse of funds.

Blending SLGBs with Public Capital for Cost-effective Debt

A lower cost of borrowing would be crucial to motivate utility companies to repurpose coal plants early. The companies could achieve this through dual-tranche issuances. The senior tranche could target institutional investors, while the subordinate tranche targets Multilateral Development Banks (MDBs) and Development Finance Institutions (DFIs). The subordinate bondholders would provide capital at a concessional rate to incentivise early coal plant repurposing. Alternatively, credit guarantees by MDBs/DFIs can lower the cost of SLGBs. Furthermore, MDBs/DFIs could offer grants to fund the re-skilling of the workforce, issuance transaction costs and the ongoing monitoring and verification costs required for a credible SLGB.

Conclusion

The proposed SLGB structure offers a pathway for public and private debt providers to participate in India's early retirement of coal plants. The mechanism would ensure issuers utilise the funds for their intended purpose. It enhances the credibility of the transaction, incentivises coal power producers to take action sooner than later and supports a just transition. Most importantly, this could be a way to support India in achieving its emissions reduction goals.

India's 'Intranational COP': Spirit of Cooperative Federalism[1]

India revised its target to reduce the carbon intensity of its GDP to 45 per cent by 2030, more ambitious than the earlier target of 34 per cent. These national carbon emission targets were globally appreciated and have further strengthened its leadership position in climate action. To achieve this, there is a strong need to rally the states and Union Territories (UTs) around this. For instance, during the unveiling of India's 'Long-Term Low-Carbon Development Strategy' at the recent COP27 Summit, the states/UTs seem to be non-participants. In line with the spirit of cooperative federalism and 'Team India', the country must leapfrog to a new paradigm of inter-state/UT cooperation on climate actions. Making states/UTs active partners can improve the efficacy of public sector actions. Using the methods that worked for Goods and Services Tax (GST) may be something that can be considered.

Role of States

Provisions in the Constitution of India, legislations of the Parliament, executive orders and judicial decisions enable states/UTs to have a substantial influence on matters pertaining to land, electricity, mobility, labour, pollution control, skill building, law and order, financial incentives for commercial activities, etc. Therefore, states/UTs can become prime movers in the last mile through interventions in policy, regulation and project implementation. During the ongoing winter session of Parliament, the Prime Minister of India also emphasised the potential of India's cooperative federalism in becoming 'a torch bearer of the world' in achieving Sustainable Development Goals (SDGs) while addressing its Rajya Sabha.

Today, though a project is conceived, financed and implemented by central agencies, site-specific mobilisation of resources requires the active cooperation of the states/UTs. An important case in point can be electricity distribution, where states can exponentially augment India's clean energy ambitions. Furthermore, they can directly support municipal corporations/village panchayats in innovating customised approaches for faster and

[1] The article was written by Labanya Prakash Jena, Vaibhav Chaudhary and Prasad Ashok Thakur and was first published by the Observer Research Foundation. https://www.orfonline.org/expert-speak/indias-intranational-cop-spirit-of-cooperative-federalism

inclusive adoption of national climate goals in line with the socioeconomic and cultural sensitivities of the region.

India's 'Intranational COP'

While many states/UTs are promulgating policies within their jurisdictions to achieve a net-zero future, the initiatives seem to be working in isolation. Climate action is a unifying theme and creating a forum similar to the Goods and Services Taxes (GST) council, which created successful engagement models during the pan-India roll-out of GST, can be helpful. This intra-country group, Intranational COP, can offer opportunities for sharing a stage across parties in a neutral setting where outcome-oriented conversations can take place. It can kindle the friendly spirit of cooperative and competitive federalism with each state/UT committing to bolder actions towards net-zero. It can potentially introduce new evaluation parameters for measuring the performance of stakeholders based on their ability to build consensus across boundaries while keeping aside their myopic and constricted vote-bank-centred politics.

It may be argued that India already has the mechanism of interstate councils to discuss interstate coordination issues. However, they have increasingly been reduced in resolving interstate disputes. Climate change, however, is a new and dynamic topic for all stakeholders. It is an equaliser where no state/UT has any inherent advantageous positions. States/UTs can learn best practices from each other to implement, achieve and measure the outcomes of their actions.

Common but Differentiated Responsibilities

It can also be a forum similar to COP but attending to intranational issues. For example, it is well-established that some parts of India are economically more developed as compared to others. This translates to the fact that the relatively more prosperous regions contribute more to India's carbon emissions. Such states are better positioned to initially invest in expensive low-carbon technologies and disseminate them to achieve economies of scale. India COP can provide a candid environment to express such issues. It can unleash creative mechanisms to offset regional imbalances while respecting local cultural sensitivities. It can provide a platform for states/UTs to forge MOUs that complement each other's strengths while filling up the gaps in technical/financial/people resources. For e.g., small hilly states have good hydroelectric power potential, but they may lack financial wherewithal;

states like Rajasthan have good solar energy potential but currently lack sufficient trained manpower, etc.

Intranational COP can be a dedicated flagship platform to thrash out a national consensus on India's climate goals and the means to achieve them. For example, the Finance Commission can play a role in allocating capital based on the climate actions and needs of states. The mechanisms of climate funding and allocation, led by the Finance Commission, can be debated and agreed upon on this platform. Such a consensus will enjoy double legitimacy as it is arrived at collectively by the union and state/UT governments. Its success can then become a template for federal nations across the world to engage with provincial/local governments with diverse socio-political and economic challenges. It can score a big win in promoting India's soft power, especially as it takes on the presidency of the G20.

Net-Zero: Erecting an Enduring Green-steel Ecosystem in India[1]

By 2030, India aims to be the world's 3rd largest economy. By ramping up its manufacturing capacity to 300 million tonnes per annum, India's steel sector will assume the role of a growth multiplier. However, steel is a highly carbon-intensive sector and contributes ~8 per cent of global CO_2 emissions. For India, the sector is responsible for 11 per cent of total emissions or about 250 $MtCO_2e$ in absolute terms. This number may rise to 600+ $MtCO_2e$ by 2045. Globally, steel is considered a 'hard-to-abate' sector. The sector is characterised by high capital intensity, complex processes, dependence on bulk raw materials, cyclical growth-profitability trends and periodic over-capacity. Such factors hinder the rapid adoption of carbon reduction technologies that are perceived to add costs to an industry with relatively low profit margins.

In recent decades, the steel industry has achieved significant reductions in energy input and CO_2 emissions intensity. Increasing use of electric arc furnace (EAFs), as well as utilisation of waste heat recovery technologies, have contributed to about 61 per cent reduction in energy consumption per tonne of steel produced since 1960. However, these improvements have not been sufficient to reduce the total absolute GHG emissions from steel production. There remains an estimated 15–20 per cent improvement potential on the energy efficiency front.

Need for Disruptive Innovations

Modern steel plants operate near the limits of practical thermodynamic efficiency. Therefore, to achieve a substantial reduction in the carbon footprint of the steel manufacturing process, development of breakthrough technologies is crucial. To achieve this, there are fundamentally two pathways: one is to introduce carbon capture technologies in tandem with existing processes to lock-in the carbon; the other is to replace carbon with 'green-reductants' such as hydrogen. Efforts are also required for optimising specific water consumption. Several digital solutions and industry 4.0

[1] The article was written by Labanya Prakash Jena and Prasad Ashok Thakur and was first published by the ET Energy World (From the *Economic Times*). https://energy.economictimes.indiatimes.com/news/power/net-zero-erecting-an-enduring-green-steel-ecosystem-in-india/97787064

techniques need to be deployed to unlock value and rapid scale-up of green steel sector value chains. A 2022 McKinsey report suggests that over the next three decades, an investment to the tune of USD 4.5 trillion is required to decarbonise production. Hence, a close working relationship must be forged between ecosystem players like governments, regulators, banks and manufacturers of steel, carbon-capture solutions and green hydrogen to enable a smooth transition and concurrent demand generation.

In Sweden, major ecosystem players like SSAB, LKAB and Vattenfall have developed a technology to utilise green hydrogen for steel manufacturing on a commercial scale and are planning to introduce it in the market within the next 3–5 years. Back home in India, in partnership with Carbon Clean, Tata Steel has operationalised a 5 tonne per day carbon-capture facility. JSW is also trying to leverage capabilities of their in-house teams to achieve differentiation through ecolabel certifications.

Catalytic Role of the Government

During early phases of a systemic transition, governments can play a crucial role in creating new value networks, marketplaces and alliances. New technologies at near market-ready stages may require a stimulus of soft loans for a controlled roll-out/scale-up. Furthermore, an ecosystem- approach can promote innovation of supplementary technologies resulting in better returns on green-investments. For example, Hydrogen direct reduction (H-DR) technology, also known as HYBRIT, uses hydrogen instead of natural gas in steel manufacturing process.

European steel companies are planning to execute its pilot trial in 2024, with the hope of 80 per cent to 90 per cent reduction of carbon emissions. However, its commercial viability depends on the cost-reduction of green hydrogen, a supplementary sector. Similarly, other upcoming technologies like electrolysis of iron-ore, molten oxide electrolysis method, pure hydrogen DRI-EAF clean technology, etc., require development of ancillary industries. Here, availability of a favourable debt capital regime for such projects can create economies of scale leading to self-sustenance.

For proven startups in priority sectors, government's early incubation support can arrive through convertible debt and equity. Startups working in breakthrough technologies for mop-up of particulate pollutants, green hydrogen, round-the-clock clean energy, etc., for the steel industry can utilise such a stimulus to leapfrog from their labs to a stage where commercial investors come onboard. Through specialised ring-fenced investment mechanisms, government/PSU incubators can become minor equity investors at an early stage where ticket sizes are small, but risk of failure is the highest. Such a mechanism allows for government's investments to be spread over several startups across adjacent sectors as well. International financial institutions can also play a role in this arena through their investment agencies.

Progressive Carbon Pricing to Incentivise R&D

As a nudge to the sector, a progressive and optimal carbon pricing regime by the government can entice steel manufactures to commit meaningful resources for R&D in green technologies. Governments can use this mopped-up carbon tax from the steel industry to offer R&D and startup support within the same sector. If successful, such breakthrough solutions stand a chance to be deployed at scale, globally. The investments made in R&D can start yielding robust returns within the first few years as the premiums earned from the domestic sale and export of 'green-steel' start pouring in.

Steel Recycling for Circular Economy

Steel's unique attribute is that it can be recycled multiple times without loss of properties. Thus, the increased availability of steel scrap can be leveraged to create circularity in business models in this sector. This can eventually cut down dependence on mining and natural resource extraction activities. Governments can also promote efficiency in the reverse logistics and steel recycling value chain through continuous upgrade of targeted policies and programmes like Perform Achieve & Trade scheme, the Steel Scrap Recycling Policy, the National Resource Efficiency Policy, PLI scheme for speciality steel, etc. Through innovative value-chain models, by-products generated during steel manufacturing like slag, processed gasses and residue can find applications in cement sector, industrial heating and zinc extraction, respectively.

As India embarks on a journey of becoming a developed nation by 2047, its steel industry should exhibit strength and resilience in the face of a dynamic global marketplace. It must de-risk supply chains, leverage digital solutions and deliver customer focused products for the world markets. The sector must operate from a position of advantage founded on strong cash flows. This will create enough headroom for making bold investments in ambitious projects to deliver sustainable value for all.

Building a Carbon Capture Ecosystem in India[1]

The peak daily concentration of carbon dioxide (CO_2) witnessed in the earth's atmosphere in 2022 is 421 parts per million (ppm). This is enough to fundamentally alter the planet's climatic equilibrium. Human activities continue to emit CO_2 at rates that far surpass the intake capacities of natural carbon sinks. The planet is fast racing towards the 550 ppm mark by 2050, which can cause irreversible and catastrophic changes to the earth's climate.

What is to be done? Only renewable energy systems cannot make hard-to-decarbonise industries such as cement and steel carbon-free. By themselves, these systems cannot alone help meet the net-zero targets. For embarking on a net-zero path, additional efforts are needed for the development and deployment of technologies that can capture, utilise and store carbon from various ecosystems on a large scale. Some of these projects have been undertaken at a pilot scale by steel, cement and petroleum companies.

India is the second-largest manufacturer of cement and steel, the third-largest consumer of energy and the fourth-largest petroleum refiner. These are 'hard to decarbonise' sectors. A recent study by the Global Carbon Capture & Storage (CCS) Institute suggests that some regions in the country may be well-suited for long-term carbon storage. India has an estimated potential of 395–614 gigatonnes (1 gigatonne equals 1 billion tonnes) of CO_2 storage in its geological sinks, 140–200 times India's annual carbon emissions. This makes India a natural home for nurturing and embracing Carbon Capture, Utilisation and Storage (CCUS) ecosystems.

CCUS facilities are energy-intensive. Previously, fossil fuels were used to power their constituent processes. Emission from these fuels was captured at the same facility, which reduced their efficiency in mopping up carbon from the target ecosystems.

Today, solar and wind energy combined with utility-scale energy storage batteries can fully replace fossil fuels at CCUS facilities. Innovation in carbon-locking materials like melamine porous networks, metal-organic frameworks (MoFs) and hierarchical nano-porous membranes (class of

[1] The article was written by Labanya Prakash Jen, Prasad Ashok Thakur, and Vikram Vishal and was first published by Gateway House. https://www.gatewayhouse.in/building-carbon-capture-ecosystem-india/#:~:text=Renewable%20energy%20systems%20on%20their,like%20petroleum%2C%20steel%20and%20cement.

nanocomposites) has made them more efficient, cost-effective and sustainable. The increased adoption of the circular economy models with a special focus on carbon value chains has re-purposed carbon as an input resource in manufacturing processes. The Europe-based Carbon4PUR initiative, consisting of chemical sector players like Covestro AG, Recticel and Megara Resins S.A., aim to utilise CO_2 from the steel industry to manufacture chemicals on a commercial scale.

As per the World Bank, more than two-thirds of countries have plans to leverage carbon markets to meet their Nationally Determined Contributions (NDCs). In line with this trend, India's Lower House of Parliament passed the Energy Conservation (Amendment) Bill, 2022, paving the way towards establishing domestic carbon markets. India can emulate countries like Chile, Singapore and Jordan which are building carbon markets backed by digital infrastructure comprising systems for monitoring, reporting and verification (MRV) with greenhouse gases (GHG) data synced to national and international registries. Emerging blockchain technologies may also support fair valuation of carbon-finance-products. Such new-age developments in carbon markets can lead to the democratisation of CCUS.

On the finance front, CCUS technologies need a large amount of patient capital for research and development (R&D). Hence, they need to tap into diverse sources of funding to evolve to a level where private investors are convinced to put in their money. Measures like tax incentives, concessional loans and grants can address the financing challenges in the further development and adoption of this technology. Startup companies in the CCUS space which may be struggling to access early-stage venture capital or angel investments, will benefit from such measures.

As a strategic initiative in CCUS, the Government of India (GoI) has established the National Centres of Excellence (CoE) for innovation in this domain. These centres are mandated to map, capture and synergise innovation and R&D activities while developing cross-functional networks between academia, industry, public sectors, startups and other relevant stakeholders. The goal is to have pilot projects which can then be scaled up if successful.

Some recent examples from the corporate world are:

- Indian Oil Corporation Limited has established an industrial CCU project
- NTPC has set up a 20-tonne per day of CO_2 capture facility, where CO_2 is converted to methanol

- Tata Steel has set up a 5-tonne per day of CO_2 capture facility
- Tuticorin Alkali Chemicals plant captures around 200 tonnes per day of CO_2, converting it to baking soda
- ONGC and Equinor have signed an MoU to collaborate on CO_2-enhanced oil recovery

India's university campuses, startups and incubation ecosystems are also making a mark on prominent forums. In a recent global competition supported by the Elon Musk Foundation, a student-led team from IIT Bombay won the XPRIZE for demonstrating a system that can remove CO_2 from gaseous industrial effluents and convert it into valuable commercial chemicals. Another startup incubated at Jawaharlal Nehru Centre for Advanced Scientific Research (JNCASR), Bengaluru, has received the National Award 2021 from the Technology Development Board of India's Department of Science and Technology, for developing efficient catalysts and methodologies for CCU processes.

Finally, like the International Solar Alliance, India can create and lead an International CCUS Alliance. India can steer global developments to make the sector more inclusive and equitable. India can provide a trusted and strategically neutral platform for creating outcome-oriented partnerships in the CCUS domain with a special focus on providing visibility to the needs and opportunities in the Least Developed Countries (LDCs) and Small Island Developing States (SIDS). By leveraging and synchronising the collective strength of its member countries, the alliance can sharpen CCUS as a potent and versatile tool in humanity's climate action armoury.

As India assumes the presidency of the G20 in December 2022, it can set the ball rolling by initiating and shaping a pragmatic discourse on CCUS. It can help define the nature and quantum of support for public-private partnerships for the upcoming decade. India's conducive CCUS ecosystem can help it emerge as a front-runner in climate action.

Mumbai and the Race to Net-Zero[1]

Cities account for over 70 per cent of global carbon emissions. Limiting global warming to 1.5°C will require rapid and far-reaching transitions in urban areas. It is heartening to see the recent announcement by Mumbai to become net-zero by 2050—the first Asian city to commit to such an ambitious target on climate action.

Given the importance of such climate initiatives in sprawling metros, Mumbai has the unique potential to embark on a larger, bolder mission to steer the entire nation toward an inclusive, resilient and net-zero future.

Mumbai the Financial Centre

Mumbai is home to large corporations, banks and financial institutions. It is also the nerve centre of financial regulations in the country. This ecosystem has enormous potential to shape India's future. The flag bearers at the helm of these institutions can influence India's climate actions.

Collective action by key stakeholders can make a meaningful change to decarbonise the economy. There is a need for consensus to establish partnerships for climate actions and the city can facilitate the creation of such a tightly knit, cohesive, sector-specific peer group. This coordination of different stakeholders can enable dialogue, build consensus, promote shared knowledge, expand expertise, consolidate existing initiatives and document and transfer best practices.

It is imperative for the city to play an important role in bringing the stakeholders together. The city can form a leadership group with members from financial and non-financial companies. For example, all the banks and financial institutions with headquarters in the city can form a coalition to facilitate financing for net-zero targets.

As divestment in carbon-emitting businesses continues, engagement with corporates is the best strategy to decarbonise the economy. As a group, they can engage with their borrowers to facilitate the transition towards net-zero. They can set and follow uniform net-zero lending and investing standards to motivate borrowers to make business decisions to achieve net-zero. They

[1] The article was written by Labanya Prakash Jena and Prasad Ashok Thakur and was first published by the World Economic Forum. https://www.weforum.org/agenda/2022/06/mumbai-and-the-race-to-net-zero/

can collectively move through proxy votes and proposals concerning climate change, thereby influencing the corporate business practices.

The leadership group can coordinate with policymakers and regulators based in Mumbai to build the right policy and regulatory mechanism to reduce carbon intensity over time.

The Example of Paris

Mumbai should emulate Paris in providing climate leadership for the region. Paris seized the opportunity to host one of the most seminal climate-action episodes in humanity's history, namely COP21. Paris' emergence as a location of choice was thanks to it being the capital of a country that has, to a large extent, decarbonised its electricity. About 90 per cent of France's electricity supply comes from clean energy sources like nuclear, hydrogen, wind and solar. Mumbai, in turn, can summon diverse stakeholders for decisive climate action.

The Brihanmumbai Municipal Corporation (BMC), armed with its Mumbai Climate Action Plan 2022, is best positioned to initiate such a move. It can provide a collaborative platform to facilitate action-oriented dialogue among corporates, financial actors and financial regulators. BMC can bring civil societies, research institutions and NGOs together to collaborate.

Mumbai is India's Financial Heartbeat

A Climate-Action-Council (CAC) can be formed through this collaborative platform, which will take the climate actions of the coalitions forward. BMC can ensure the success of its unique endeavour by becoming an active contributor to the CAC's resource pool. It can provide smart incentives to corporates based in Mumbai and provide partial relaxation/rebate/reduction of property tax to organisations that pledge and deliver on the milestones towards achieving net-zero.

BMC's critical role in Mumbai's electricity distribution and public mobility sectors (through Brihanmumbai Electric Supply and Transport Undertaking) provides it with unique and powerful levers to offer tangible financial incentives to boost faster adoption of climate-smart actions by corporates and their employees. Moreover, it can offer at concessional rates outdoor advertisement avenues on BEST vehicles, bus stops, street furniture and digital billboards to showcase climate actions. Such initiatives can entice more stakeholders to join the net-zero march.

Mumbai can infuse a fresh burst of ingenuity in India's climate actions. It can change climate interactions from being confrontation to collaborative. Mumbai's efforts could prove that local and regional initiatives can have a sizable impact on the fight against climate change. If Mumbai pulls this off, India's own march to net-zero will be all the more possible.

FINANCING GREEN AND GREENING FINANCE

A Four-step Regulatory Solution for a Climate-aligned Transition of Banks and Financial Institutions[1]

Climate change is a global event impacting people the world over. The climate change risk is not only restricted to the real economy but could potentially threaten the financial system's stability through quick value erosion of financial assets. The historical and current relationship between climate change and the financial system is weak. However, cautionary notices of the significant financial risks from climate change strengthened this relationship in the last couple of years. The association has become more evident in recent years with mounting business losses due to increased occurrence and intensity of extreme weather incidences such as storms, floods and droughts. The sudden or gradual loss in business could lead to a mass decline in the value of financial assets.

The two major divisions of climate change risks are the Physical and Transition risks. The physical risks are related to severe weather events, changes in precipitation patterns, extreme variability in weather patterns, rising mean temperatures and sea levels. Transition risk is related to business losses caused by a change in policies and regulations to mitigate climate change risks, a drastic decline in the cost of adopting climate-friendly substitute products due to technology disruption and a preference for climate-friendly products in the market. All these risks would adversely affect the productivity of assets, increase the cost of operation, disrupt the supply chain and reduce the market demand for carbon-emitting or polluting businesses. These disruptions could adversely affect borrowers' credit profiles, increase the default risk of loans and bonds, suddenly depress equity prices and create stranded assets in the financial system.

The Reserve Bank of India (RBI), in its Annual Report 2019–20, observed, 'Given that the impact of climate change on India is expected to be one of the severest globally, the need for an appropriate framework to identify, assess and manage financial risks arising out of climate risk has become an imperative.'

---

[1] The article was written by Labanya Prakash Jena and Vaibhav Pratap Singh and was first published by the ET BFSI (From the *Economic Times*). https://bfsi.economictimes.indiatimes.com/news/industry/a-four-step-regulatory-solution-for-a-climate-aligned-transition-of-banks-and-financial-institutions/92435879

Hence the financial regulators in India need to correct the financial systems by designing financial regulations to assess the risks correctly and reward green investments. RBI has taken certain steps to correct the market failure and accelerate lending to the green sector. However, the central bank needs to step up and follow the best practices in financial regulation to mitigate climate change risk. We recommend the following steps to correct the market failure and for adoption by the regulators.

Climate-related Supervisory Risk Framework

The first step is to measure individual financial institutions' transition and physical risk exposure and incorporate these risks within the supervisory risk framework. The adequacy of a bank's capital is a function of its risk profile. The supervisors expect banks to consider all risks affecting capital, including risks that might have an indirect or slowly developing impact. Climate-related and environmental risks are drivers of existing prudential risk categories.

Climate Risk Integration

The second is to develop the national guidelines for climate risk integration basis the climate risks and stress testing them to understand the capital adequacy. Many central banks and other financial regulators worldwide have warned that climate and environmental risks could fundamentally affect their core mandate of maintaining financial stability. A climate risk stress test is an essential tool to address these challenges. It can shed light on the potential impact of severe but plausible climate scenarios that may occur but for which no historical precedent is available.

Differential Capital Adequacy Norms

The third is adopting differential capital adequacy norms, allowing climate risk-based weights to calculate institutions' capital adequacy. As per the BIS/Basel Accord, the fundamental premise of banking regulation is to provide adequate capital against unexpected losses and price expected losses. Basel II and Basel III (integrated), the most critical and prudential global banking regulations, aim to strengthen the banks' regulation and supervision worldwide by providing guidelines for weighing risks for capital provision. Some financial regulators across Europe have suggested that reevaluating the current risk weights would be required based on risks presented by climate change. Research in China indicates that allocating more green loans to the total loan portfolio can reduce a bank's overall Non-Performing Loans (NPL) ratio. Experts believe such a move could also help reduce the credit risk of the banking portfolio.

Building Database and Analytical Capability

The fourth is that the central bank needs to develop research and analytical capabilities to assess climate risk better. Identify the data required to support their policy objectives and collect and collate data to support financial policies, regulations and risk assessment. Besides, it should enhance its statistical infrastructure to keep related climate-related data collection and use it for policy and regulatory decision-making. The data points on climate-related risk are not historical, but forward looking. So, the central bank needs to rely on climate change indicators, countries' energy transition plans and borrowers' transition plans and scenario analysis on a macro level.

Though not a substitute for the fiscal policy, e.g., subsidies and penalties for labour-intensive sectors to reward more climate aligned investments, the above steps will help increase the flow of finance and reduce the climate risks in banking portfolios.

Greening NBFID: How India's New Institution for Development Finance can Help Meet its Sustainable Funding Needs[1]

At COP26 this year, India presented five nectar elements to deal with the challenge of climate change. According to these Panchamrit principles, by 2030, India aims to increase its non-fossil fuel-based energy capacity to 500 GW, meet 50 per cent of its energy requirements using renewable energy and reduce the economy's carbon intensity to less than 45 per cent. Between now and 2030, the country has set a target to reduce its projected carbon emissions by one billion tonnes. Lastly, it has committed to becoming carbon neutral and achieving net-zero emissions by the year 2070.

What is interesting is that these announcements come in the same year the National Bank for Financing Infrastructure and Development (NBFID) Act, 2021, established a development financial institution (DFI) that offers long-term non-recourse financing for the various segments of the economy where risks are too high for commercial investors. Could this provide the leverage India needs to meet its sustainable funding needs?

What Does India Need to Achieve its Climate Goals?

The country needs to invest a massive amount of capital in climate change mitigation projects, including renewable energy, energy efficiency, clean transportation, etc., in the next five decades to meet its global commitments. Besides, India also needs to invest heavily in climate adaptation as the impact of climate change risk is imminent. In comparison to climate mitigation, climate adaptation gets less attention as its benefits are restricted to a particular region.

It is noteworthy here that India is one of the most climate-vulnerable countries in the world. It is ranked 7th in Germanwatch's Global Climate Risk Index. Rising daily temperatures are leading to frequent extreme weather events. The National Disaster Management Authority estimates that 58.6 per cent of the landmass is vulnerable to moderate to very highly intensive earthquakes; 12 per cent of the land is prone to flood and river erosion. Out

---

[1] The article was written by Labanya Prakash Jena and Shreyansh Jain and was first published by CarbonCopy. https://carboncopy.info/greening-nbfid-how-indias-new-institution-for-development-finance-can-help-meet-its-sustainable-funding-needs/

of the 7,516 km coastline, 5,700 km is exposed to cyclones and tsunamis; 68 per cent of the cultivable land is at risk of drought and 15 per cent of the landmass is vulnerable to landslides and avalanches. In 2018 alone, India's economic loss due to climate change was estimated at $37 billion (about 0.36 per cent of its GDP), impacting multiple sectors like housing, infrastructure, construction, etc. Clearly, the country needs to invest significantly in climate adaptation projects, including building sea walls, strengthening disaster early warning systems and developing drought and flood management infrastructure. In this pursuit, long-term and low-cost capital is a critical enabler of India's climate action.

Although there is no precise estimate on capital requirements to achieve climate goals, there is a consensus among forecasters that India needs trillions of dollars of capital to meet its climate goals. In the renewable energy sector alone, India needs more than $500 billion to reach its target of 500 GW by 2030. There are trillions of dollars required to decarbonise its electricity system and hard-to-decarbonise industries, transportation, agriculture and climate adaptation projects over the next fifty years. Most of the financing requirements are long term and are associated with high real and/or perceived risk.

How can NBFID Clear the Way for Sustainable Green Finance?

Presently, the lack of a climate/green finance taxonomy, poor incentives for borrowers to invest in green projects, unproven business models, long-term financing needs, limited information and bankability validation constraints private financers from funding projects related to climate change. There is a need to align India's financial sector with organised efforts to accelerate green lending and investment. The NBFID can play an important role in countering markets and financial institutions' aversion to lending to risky projects and ensuring the availability of resources at a relatively lower cost of capital. Attracting large-scale public capital can play a catalytic role in addressing what is arguably the country's biggest growth and developmental challenge.

Several businesses and projects pertaining to climate actions have the same characteristics as infrastructure projects. Some of them are—natural monopoly, high-sunk costs, non-tradability of output and bestowing of externalities on society. Some of these projects belong to the infrastructure sector, such as utility-scale renewable energy projects, green-energy corridor, battery charging infrastructure, climate-resilient infrastructure for drought and flood management and sustainable mass rapid transportation systems. Without public financial support, it isn't easy to scale and sustain these projects.

The NBFID has been mandated to lend, invest and offer financial solutions which can attract private capital for infrastructure projects. It can bridge the gap in long-term financing of projects for India's climate actions by contributing both direct financing and also providing a supportive, collaborative environment to catalyse private finance for those counterparties that would otherwise struggle to attract investment. It can offer a range of financial products to pump the economic credit engine and support companies and projects that might otherwise be considered too risky—typically due to the project's length, type, or geography. NBFID will achieve two goals—meeting policy objectives to overcome market failures in projects and meet sustainable development needs.

India is leading two international institutional initiatives to encourage environment-friendly investments and divert capital from carbon-emitting sectors to carbon-mitigating sectors, namely the International Solar Alliance (ISA) and the Coalition for Disaster Resilient Infrastructure (CDRI). The former has a target to mobilise investments of more than $1 trillion by 2030 and the latter aims to promote the resilience of new and existing infrastructure systems to climate and disaster risks. The NBFID can be positioned as a green financial institution to play a catalytic role in supporting these two global initiatives—lend or invest or design financial solutions to attract capital.

Lack of information for decision-making and high transaction costs associated with modelling climate risk scenarios often impede investments in adaptation projects. The NBFID can mainstream adaptation in lending operations by prioritising disbursement of funds to borrowers that display a commitment to international frameworks on climate change. Furthermore, as sustainability and climate change are growing as a thematic investment class among investors, the NBFID can design innovative financial instruments to source funds from capital markets, government and multilateral institutions. These instruments can include long-tenor loans, green/climate-resilient bonds, credit-enhancement mechanisms, credit guarantees, etc. Besides, it can conduct due diligence of green projects on behalf of other government and multilateral institutions that do not have the capacity and know-how to appraise these projects.

Today, the government is looking at the NBFID as 'necessary to act as a provider, enabler, and catalyst for infrastructure financing.' Like infrastructure, a cog to economic growth and development, climate change projects aim to make the economy resilient and allow it to maintain healthy growth. Besides, they hold similar characteristics of infrastructure projects, hence warrant urgent attention. NBFID can be the right institution to help India's transition to a sustainable economy and demonstrate its commitment to climate action.

Why Regulators Need to Emphasise the Value of Sustainability to Investors and Asset Managers[1]

Investment advisors function under a blanket of fiduciary obligations. These require them to undertake the duty of loyalty which includes acting in good faith and avoiding conflicts of interest and observing prudence when it comes to the conduct of due diligence and protecting the interests of investors. The decisions made by investors ultimately trickle down the investment chain and affect the way companies are managed and operated.

Empirical and academic evidence suggests that sustainability issues are financially material and can generate investment value. Hence, analysis of sustainable components can aid investors in identifying the material issues in investment decision-making. The ignorance of sustainability issues in investment analysis could lead to mispricing of securities and poor investment decisions—effectively, a failure of fiduciary duty.

Sustainability is a systemic issue that could significantly alter securities pricing in some sectors, industries and geographies. It follows that the incorporation of sustainability issues is a core characteristic of a prudent investment process. As policies and regulations around sustainability change around the world, the investment value of companies to accentuate sustainability will also likely change to keep step. A report, 'Fiduciary Duty in the 21st Century', by the Principle of Responsible Investment (PRI) and United Nations Environment Programme Finance Initiative (UNEP FI), demonstrates the critical importance of incorporating ESG standards into the regulatory array of fiduciary duty. The report suggests that 'failure to consider all long-term investment value drivers, including ESG issues, is a failure of fiduciary duty.' Financial regulators should clarify for asset managers such as pension funds, insurance companies and mutual funds in the appropriate directives that sustainability must be incorporated in the investment decision-making process to ensure that their fiduciary duty is respected. This is a glaring gap in India, where sustainability is not emphasised as a significant factor in the fiduciary norm for investors and asset managers.

---

[1] The article was written by Labanya Prakash Jena and Rajashree Padmanabhi and was first published by CarbonCopy. https://carboncopy.info/why-regulators-need-to-emphasise-the-value-of-sustainability-to-investors-and-asset-managers/

Financial regulators, such as SEBI, PFRDA and IRDA, are yet to make clear in the directives to investors and asset managers to incorporate financially material sustainability issues in-stock selection, risk management and asset allocation. Besides, the directives must make it mandatory for asset managers and fund managers to disclose and report the steps taken by investors and asset managers concerning sustainability in their fiduciary duty.

Employ Stewardship and Active Ownership

Another key component of stewardship is engaging mentor active ownership practices of investors and asset managers. Stewardship or active ownership is a concept that encourages investors and asset managers to play an active role in investment decision-making, including directly and indirectly influencing corporates to make certain business decisions to enhance the value of their investment. Stewardship or active ownership is becoming an important part of these investor fiduciary duties and in addressing sustainability risks in the portfolio.

The financial industry, particularly asset managers and institutional investors, use various active ownership tactics to influence corporates to identify sustainability issues and incorporate them in business decision-making. For example, oil and gas giant Shell recently committed to taking significant additional action on climate change, including a commitment to achieve net-zero emissions as a result of active engagement from investors led by the Church of England Pension Board and Robeco among others. Globally, asset management companies and institutional investors are widely deploying active ownership as a tool to exert pressure on the corporates to take necessary actions to reduce carbon emissions. Active engagement by institutional investors can include management of risks concerning sustainability and disclose their engagement reports to beneficiaries on the same.

The Financial Stability and Development Council (FSDC) is an apex institutional body set up to strengthen the mechanisms for maintaining financial stability, financial sector development and inter-regulatory coordination in India. In 2018, the FSDC approved a common stewardship code in consultation with the SEBI, IRDA and PFRDA. The stewardship code includes engagement with corporates on governance matters, issues related to poor financial performance, leadership and any other risks. In addition, the codes warrant investors to exercise independent judgment in proxy voting and disclose stewardship practices. The code provides guidelines for the institutional investors to formulate a comprehensive policy detailing the monitoring and reporting mechanisms.

Although the SEBI Stewardship Code has ESG compliance norms, it does not have the wherewithal to force investors to follow the norms in spirit—there is no penalty prescribed in case of non-compliance. South African Stewardship Code considers ESG norms as a law under their Pension Funds Act, 1956, while Hongkong Code has emphasised the adoption of ESG norms in its Stewardship Code. These two countries have made non-compliance with ESG norms punishable for investors. The Indian financial regulators can make sustainability norms strict and enforceable instead of just a passing reference.

Investors can implement stewardship in various approaches to influence investee companies. These include: engaging with corporates to support and encourage them to transition the businesses to less carbon-intensive and less pollutive; raising questions about sustainability issues in the Annual General Meeting (AGM) and making sustainability issues a board agenda when exercising direct control over corporates.

Financed GHG Emissions: A Case of Regulatory Porosity[1]

Post COVID-19, Indian financial regulators, particularly the Reserve Bank of India (RBI) and the Securities & Exchange Board of India (SEBI), developed a slew of climate change guidelines and norms focusing on Disclosure as a means to help attain the transparency required for market incentives to operate efficiently.

Financed Emissions, and Why is it Critical?

A critical point on Disclosure is 'financed emissions' which, in essence, represents greenhouse gas (GHG) emissions produced as an end result of the investments or loans provided by banks and financial institutions. This is a pre-requisite to understanding the climate-related transition risk of loans and investments; in other words, how loans and investments by banks and FIs contribute to GHG emissions. The Greenhouse Gas Protocol classifies financed emissions under the Scope 3 emissions category meant for banks and financial institutions. Scope 3 includes indirect emissions of an organisation excluding the purchase and use of electricity, steam, heating and cooling.

SEBI's Business Responsibility and Sustainability Reporting (BRSR) on climate-related regulation is restricted to the top 1,000 companies by market capitalisation and by Scope 1 and Scope 2 emissions. Although several banks and financial institutions come in the top 1,000 list, this regulation mandates companies to disclose only their Scope 1 and Scope 2 emissions, leaving out Scope 3 where their real emissions are. Scope 3 emissions contribute an average of 95 per cent of the total financed emissions of banks and financial institutions—a staggering indicator of its significance in climate change.

To add to this, RBI's recent Report on Currency and Finance suggests that the exposure of Indian banks to high energy-intensive sectors like generation and distribution of energy (utility sector) and industrial sector (steel, cement and chemicals) is relatively high. Besides this, Non-Banking Financial Companies (NBFCs) provide approximately 50 per cent of their gross credit to carbon-intensive power and automobile segments. Moreover,

[1] The article was written by Labanya Prakash Jena and Dhruba Purkayastha and was first published by the *Financial Express*. https://www.financialexpress.com/opinion/financed-ghg-emissions-a-case-of-regulatory-porosity/3291049/

around 6 per cent of NBFC credit is exposed to Micro, Small and Medium Enterprises (MSMEs) that typically depend on conventional fuel.

Since it is not mandatory for banks and financial institutions to disclose Scope 3 emissions, it is challenging to quantify financed emissions in the financial system. Also, borrowers or investee companies do not disclose Scope 3 emissions even if they are bound to follow the BRSR framework. MSMEs that do not come under BRSR, are also not mandated to disclose GHG emissions. Effectively, it becomes extremely difficult for banks and FIs to assess financed emissions. This, despite the fact that climate change is considered a systemic risk to the financial system. Moreover, it is not possible for equity investors and bondholders or even regulators of these institutions to differentiate among financiers on the basis of the carbon intensity of loans and investments.

The Need of the Hour

Mandatory financed-emissions disclosure by banks and FIs is the need of the hour. A light format of BRSR for MSMEs, at least limited to GHG emissions, could be followed. Another method to assess GHG emissions could be to consider an industry average of GHG emissions, multiplied by the capacity or revenue of the borrower. These changes will bring about greater transparency on the role of banks and FIs in GHG emissions and how it has changed over time. It will help policymakers, regulators and the public have a better understanding of how capital is contributing to GHG emissions. Financial regulators can also better assess the transition risks of banks and FIs through their financed emissions disclosures. This in turn will nudge banks and FIs to reduce their exposure to carbon-intensive sectors and divert their capital to low-carbon businesses. It would also help banks and FIs measure the carbon intensity of their portfolios and use it as a baseline to set carbon reduction targets.

The Partnership for Carbon Accounting Financials (PCAF)—an international coalition of financial institutions—has developed a harmonised accounting approach for FIs to assess and disclose the GHG emissions associated with their loans and investments.

The PCAF standard is considered the de facto standard for measuring GHG emissions associated with financing activities; it is endorsed by the GHG Protocol and is referenced in the Task Force on Climate-related Financial Disclosure (TCFD) supplementary guidance (now a part of the International Sustainability Standards Board formed by IFRS Foundation) for the financial industry. The first step of the methodology is calculating the absolute emissions of the entity being lent to or invested in. The financed emissions can be calculated by multiplying an attribution factor. The attribution factor represents the financial institution's proportional share of lending or investment in the borrower or investee. For example, a bank has lent to a company with a total enterprise value (total equity + debt) of 100 crore and the company is generating 1,000 GHG tonnes. The bank's outstanding loan amount is 5 crore. The financed emissions of the bank will be 200 GHG tonnes (attribution factor – 20 per cent).

Reporting and disclosure of financed emissions is of critical importance to enable financial regulators and policymakers to assess the quantum of financial assets exposed to climate change risk, thereby allowing them to make informed and appropriate climate-friendly decisions.

How can You Spot 'Greenwashing'?[1]

Decarbonisation, net-zero and sustainability are buzzwords increasingly gaining currency among corporates and financial markets, and at the same time, 'greenwashing' makes regulators, investors and climate evangelists increasingly suspicious of these terminologies.

In the last few years, several companies have upped the game by declaring net-zero targets well ahead of their national timelines. Some are spending a fortune in creating a media or social media blitz to showcase their intentions/actions in their fight against climate change to 'save the world'.

Clever use of keywords, setting ambitious targets for emission reductions, issuance of green bonds in domestic/international capital markets, joining green investor coalitions, etc., are all part of the game. However, the impact on the ground has so far been lacklustre. Hence, academics and environmentalists are questioning the credibility of their intentions.

From an investors' perspective, particularly those with a long-term horizon, it is important to decipher such optics minutely. Some corporates are genuinely committed to the decarbonisation agenda, while others may be indulging in public relations (PR) gimmicks to buy more time to deliver on emission reduction targets. Such companies opine that PR exercises can shield them against the wrath of civil society and climate-conscious investors and regulators.

Although ESG rating agencies are trying to assign scores based on their evaluation of companies' climate actions, the objectivity of their methodology is questioned. There are also divergences in ESG scores across rating agencies. Thus, there is a need to develop an eye for spotting if a company's decarbonisation plan is real or just another PR exercise.

Is there a Technically Feasible Abatement Path?

For the start, establishing the company's baseline carbon intensity is critical. It can allow stakeholders to gauge if the company's offerings are less carbon-intensive when compared with the industry peers. It is to be noted that options for decarbonisation vary across sectors and geographies and involve choosing an array of technologies at various price points. Considering this

[1] The article was written by Labanya Prakash Jena and Prasad Ashok Thakur and was first published by the ET Energy World (From the *Economic Times*). https://energy.economictimes.indiatimes.com/news/renewable/how-can-you-spot-greenwashing/107255182

intricacy, the key question one must ask is whether the decarbonisation plan proposed by the company is technically feasible.

Here, technologies that allow for an absolute reduction in GHG footprint along with a unit-level reduction in GHG footprint should be preferred. If companies in certain sectors face high technological barriers to meeting their decarbonisation timelines while maintaining/improving business health, the announcement of aggressive net-zero or deep decarbonisation plans can be a matter of suspicion.

For example, presently available scientific literature suggests that green cement can achieve cost competitiveness with conventional cement in the long run (10+ years horizon). Any corporation announcing to decarbonise the cement industry in the next five years should attract close scrutiny.

Is the Abatement Path Financially Viable?

Low-cost abatement options appear desirable, but in certain sectors, they are not the easiest to implement. The key is the cost of decarbonisation technologies and how rapidly this is expected to decline to allow companies to adapt without compromising their Return on Investment (ROI). Another argument is that decarbonisation can reduce the future climate risk exposure of the company. Here, climate finance instruments must be designed in a manner to decrease the cost of capital for introducing climate-tech at the desired pace. It should also be in alignment with the ROI expectations of the investors.

Investors must assess if the company has a sufficient cash balance or is expected to generate sufficient cash flows or raise fresh capital to decarbonise its businesses at a reasonable rate. The key is whether new investment in low-carbon technologies is value additive in the long run. The eagerness to invest in low-carbon technologies may entail reduced profits in the short term while making the business climate resilient and sustainable.

Are the Decarbonisation Targets Coherently Achieved in a Phase-wise Manner?

Is the company giving themselves sufficient time to reach the intended target? A company may face interdisciplinary challenges in deploying the new climate technologies. The cost of low-carbon technology might not have been reduced meaningfully to use the technology without compromising the ROI. The carbon pricing or any other policy measures may not be stringent in the company's jurisdiction to justify deployment of low-carbon technology that can help the company to decarbonise while remaining competitive in the industry and maintaining the desired ROI.

Secondly, it is worth checking if the company has strategised its larger decarbonisation journey with a coherent bottom-up approach. Each of its business units and hierarchies should organically contribute to the organisation's larger goal. Such contributions can also be phased as short-term, medium-term and long-term missions.

Simultaneously, the company must demonstrate unequivocally its divestments from the carbon-intensive businesses, while reinvesting money in low-carbon capabilities. Here, benchmarking with peer organisations can bring in fresh perspectives. The company's capex and R&D portfolio can also throw light on the company's future offerings. Taking a holistic value chain approach, one must verify if it is moving to partner with suppliers/channel players that are equally/more aggressively implementing the decarbonisation agenda. This can help the company remain ahead of the curve to address potential issues arising from upcoming regulations and Scope 3 emission standards. Any discrepancy in these data points can delegitimise the company's decarbonisation claims.

While it is understandable that corporations aspire to portray themselves as socially responsible entities, it is crucial for them to avoid overstating their commitments. Striking a balance is essential, as companies should not make claims that exceed their realistic capabilities. From an investor's standpoint, it becomes imperative to differentiate between companies that are genuinely committed and possess a well-thought-out plan for executing their aspirations and those that may encounter technical and financial obstacles in fulfilling their promises.

Green Energy Transition in Developing Nations: High Interest Rates in Developed Nation could Disrupt the Transition[1]

As the dust settles on COP29 in Dubai, a list of new commitments unveils themselves. Among these commitments are tripling renewable energy (RE) capacities in developing nations by 2030 and upended financial assistance for them to accelerate clean energy transition. Far away from Dubai, a critical decision is taken inadvertently that can upset these ambitions.

Central Banks on both sides of the Atlantic have adopted a proactive stance to control inflation by increasing interest rates. This has resulted in skyrocketing capital costs that inadvertently disrupt the progress of the transition, especially in developing nations, where the cost of capital is ~2–3x of advanced economies and/or China. The clean energy transition is heavily dependent on the installation of new infrastructure and, therefore, highly susceptible to interest rates, affecting not just RE but also other critical sectors like electric vehicles (EVs), green hydrogen (GH2) and allied industries. All these technologies heavily rely on low-cost capital to compete with fossil fuel-intensive energy systems and make them affordable to scale up their adoption.

A significant challenge arising from escalating interest rates is the disproportionate impact on the cost of RE projects compared to traditional fossil fuel power plants. Since these projects are heavy on Capital Expenditure, rising interest rates significantly increase their costs, especially the cost of debt capital for both greenfield initiatives and refinancing of existing ones.

For instance, rising interest rates increase the cost of borrowing for entities that rely on foreign capital, compelling them to absorb this increase in capital costs or halt investments in green assets until interest rates show a meaningful decline. Given the shorter tenure of debt financing in RE compared to similar industries, business entities in developing nations find themselves in a position where they have to refinance projects at higher rates—a scenario that's undesirable yet inevitable. Besides, on the macroeconomic level, capital

[1] The article was written by Labanya Prakash Jena and Prasad Ashok Thakur and was first published by the ET Energy World (From the *Economic Times*). https://energy.economictimes.indiatimes.com/news/renewable/green-energy-transition-in-developing-nations-high-interest-rates-in-developed-nation-could-disrupt-the-transition/106513852

outflows from developing to developed countries to take advantage of higher interest rates in the latter countries also increase developing countries' sovereign risk by burdening them further on their debt servicing ability.

The International Energy Agency (IEA) has acknowledged the adverse impact of high-interest rates, expecting a pause in RE projects addition in 2024. Similarly, Bloomberg New Energy Finance (BNEF) predicts a decrease in RE investments in 2024, marking the first decline in five years. The repercussions, however, extend beyond RE to encompass electric vehicles and allied sectors like charging infrastructure. Higher borrowing costs dissuade households and businesses from purchasing capital-heavy electric vehicles. Furthermore, ancillary green technologies such as green hydrogen (GH2), transmission and distribution lines and charging stations, need low-cost debt capital for deployment. In addition, small and medium-sized companies could postpone their plans to invest in low-carbon technologies that include rooftop solar, off-grid solar infrastructure and energy-efficient technologies. Corporations may also postpone their plans to raise new debt capital or scale down their capital expenditure in clean technologies, further delaying the progress of the energy transition.

Another key channel of disruption is the movement of foreign investors to developed countries due to attractive, low-risk treasury returns. Such movements divert capital away from developing countries and limit capital for green projects. It also exerts pressure on local currencies, making domestic borrowing expensive and unaffordable. Besides, the lower availability of capital also leads to further increases in the cost of domestic capital, reducing both the bankability and profitability of projects like RE. Moreover, it increases the credit default risk on existing renewable energy projects. An increase in the risk of default may lead to a lower rating of these projects, which signals domestic banks, investors and FIs to be cautious of such projects, cutting off access to both the banking system and capital markets.

Finally, rising interest rates also cast a shadow on equity investment returns in existing renewable energy projects, diminishing investors' appetite for new projects. The rising cost of debt drives up the cost of equity investment as well, potentially rendering several projects unviable, at least in the short term, reducing the attractiveness of critical sectors. The increase in both equity and debt costs increases the cost of service delivery/operation, e.g., the levelised cost of electricity (LCOE) for RE and triggers the risk of uptake/offtake/adoption.

In sum, the combination of rising interest rates and access to affordable financing poses significant disruption to the clean energy transition in developing countries through three major channels. First, it delays the progress of the transition by obstructing the deployment of critical technologies. Second, it deters both consumers and businesses from adopting such technologies who see them as significantly expensive, at least in the short term. And finally, it diverts critical capital away from such technologies, both from domestic and foreign sources.

Overcoming these obstacles will require innovative financial solutions, international cooperation and a renewed commitment to sustainability through meaningful public intervention. Innovative financial solutions that can mitigate the risk of high interest rates could be interest rate swap options. However, these could be expensive for borrowers in developing countries. Here, international cooperation is required to subsidise interest rate swap options to make them affordable. In the short term, till interest declines substantially, international institutions must expand their financial support to developing nations as quickly as possible to keep the energy transition on track.

Financing Green Housing[1]

Housing is a major greenhouse gas (GHG) emitting sector, consuming about 24 per cent of the country's electricity and emitting over 20 per cent of total GHG. These percentages are expected to increase as housing demand accelerates, jeopardising India's green transition targets.

Conventional housing materials such as concrete and steel are made with energy-intensive processes. Also, households' electricity consumption has trebled from 2000 to 2017. This is projected to surge eight times over 2018–50, as climate change effects such as heat waves increase heavy-duty HVAC appliances and refrigerator usages. There is a need to reimagine the mindset towards the sector. The use of low-carbon materials, following sustainable construction processes and recycling building materials can lower the GHG footprint. An appropriate blend of active and passive design elements when constructing can reduce energy usage by over 35 per cent.

Retrofitting roofs, windows and doors that have higher energy performance can reduce heating and cooling demands by up to 40 per cent. Replacing incandescent lights with LEDs reduces energy consumption by about 80 per cent. But builders have no economic incentives to implement sustainability, as 'green' homes do not command premium pricing. Buyers have no motivation to pay more, especially if it is rented out. To mitigate the risk due to lower-than-expected performance of energy-saving measures, manufacturer guarantees and warranties can be augmented with standardised performance certifications from government agencies.

Financial Interventions

Even if there is an intent, finding capital is not easy. Commercial banks are unlikely to provide debt as they wish to avoid an increase in the 'loan-value to house-value' ratio. Similarly, banks rarely provide capital for retrofitting as the borrowers are reluctant to provide their houses as collateral. This is a classic case of market failure that warrants public policy interventions.

Additionally, the government and Multilateral Development Banks (MDBs) and Domestic Development Banks (DDBs) can support green housing sector through a credit enhancement mechanism. For instance,

[1] The article was written by Labanya Prakash Jena and Prasad Ashok Thakur and was first published by the *Hindu Business Line*. https://www.thehindubusinessline.com/opinion/financing-green-housing/article66083051.ece

a subordinate loan can be funded by these institutions to cover only the incremental cost of construction and design of energy-efficient houses. The savings from these houses over a period can be used to pay the loan back. An alternative is for DDBs and MDBs to offer partial credit guarantees on energy-efficient homes that pay the lender if the borrower defaults. These schemes have been used in the past to support lending by commercial banks to underserved segments and can work for the green housing sector. Similar models can be used for retrofitting existing houses.

A 'green price premium' can also be accrued from the resale of such properties. The National Housing Bank (NHB) launched SUNREF Green Housing programme in association with the French Development Agency (AFD) and the European Union (EU). NHB can test these innovative financing solutions to attract private capital to green housing. Energy-efficient projects in the housing sector are financially feasible. In China, green housing mortgage securities are traded at a premium over conventional ones. In Singapore, Green Mark (GM) rated properties are expected to fetch a higher market premium. Hence, private financers can generate an expected return from such transactions. Through innovative financing models and policies, public institutions can nudge the private players to fund the much-needed low-carbon housing sector.

How to Mobilise Climate-smart Agriculture Finance[1]

Agriculture is a significant contributor to climate change, responsible for approximately 20 per cent of global greenhouse gas (GHG) emissions and about 45 per cent of total high-temperature absorbing methane emissions. The Food and Agriculture Organisation (FAO) states that for the past two decades, the contribution of agriculture to the world's GDP has been stable at 4 per cent while farm-gate GHG went up by 13 per cent.

Conversely, climate-induced events such as increased temperatures, changes in precipitation patterns and extreme weather events, adversely impact global agriculture. Without global action, the World Bank predicts that about 43 million people in Africa alone may fall below the poverty line by 2030. International Food Policy Research Institute (IFPRI) has warned that climate change may push 90 million Indians towards hunger by 2030 due to a decline in agricultural production and disruption in the food supply chain.

Climate-smart Agriculture can Reduce GHG Emission While Increasing the Incomes of Small and Marginal Farmers

Climate-smart agriculture can combat GHG emissions by reducing emission intensity, while improving farm productivity and increasing the incomes of small and marginal farmers. Climate-smart agriculture practices, such as zero-emissions on-farm machinery and equipment, variable rate fertilisation, dry direct seeding, low- or no-tillage and animal feed mix optimisation, can reduce emissions while maintaining food production levels.

Climate-smart Agriculture Needs Out-of-the-box Solutions

However, it requires action from the more than 856 million people employed in agriculture. Reducing emissions is challenging, due to the risk of accepting lower yields in the short-term, even for long-term gains. Furthermore, new farm practices and technologies must reach small-scale farms, which produce 30–34 per cent of the food supply and account for about 75 per cent of farms. Additionally, the small-scale and fragmented composition of the farming sector in most developing countries compounds

[1] The article was written by Labanya Prakash Jena and Prasad Ashok Thakur and was first published by the World Economic Forum. https://www.weforum.org/agenda/2023/05/climate-smart-agriculture-finance/

the difficulty in demonstrating the aggregated potential of the sector to achieve positive climate outcomes at scale. Policymakers don't focus on agriculture emissions, with only 38 per cent of agriculture emissions covered in nationally determined contributions (NDC) under the Paris Agreement.

Financing Climate-smart Farming is a Bigger Challenge in Developing Countries

Traditional constraints on financing climate-smart initiatives in agriculture stem from perceptions of low profitability of agriculture, high perceived and actual risks and high transaction costs due to ineffective linkages between financers and smallholder farmers. Hence, financers often erect several barriers to limit their portfolio's exposure to agriculture by charging high-interest rates and elevating the qualifying criteria for lending. This market-distorting stance limits the capacity and skills to identify the financial needs of agriculture to implement adaptation and mitigation projects. It limits investments and the proliferation of climate-smart initiatives.

Financing Required Across the Agriculture Value Chain

Significant upfront investments are required to execute agriculture's transformation towards achieving the triple goals of combating climate change by reducing emission intensity, improving farm productivity and increasing the incomes of small and marginal farmers. Financing is needed across the value chain of agriculture. To reduce GHG emissions, significant financing is required to adopt low-carbon emitting farm machinery and equipment, lower GHG intensive animal farming practices (enteric fermentation, manure storage, animal management), and follow System of Rice Intensification (SRI). On the other hand, significant financing is required to develop drought resilient seeds, adopt water-harvesting systems, change agriculture practices and offer access to extension services and information on climate-resilient agriculture practices. Most of the activities, particularly for small farmers, need public financing support.

Deploy Public Finance Judiciously

Deploying public finance (sourced from governments, multilateral agencies, climate funds, etc.) is essential to nudge farmers to adopt climate-resilient practices. However, it can unlock resources from the private sector for farming practices that are profitable. For example, following SRI is profitable after one or two years. Solutions deployed by financers under such architecture must be infused with flexibilities in repayment conditions to match the cash flows of the local farming communities and agri-entrepreneurs. An effective blend of instruments like grants, project-based soft loans, debt, guarantees, insurances, etc., can emanate from cross-functional collaboration. This support can be tempered with a structured, objective and transparent due diligence process. Such an approach can manage risks and deliver real impact while earning requisite returns.

Create an Enabling Ecosystem

To achieve climate-smart outcomes, entry points for directing climate finance toward smallholder farmers should be created. An enabling ecosystem can be set up to facilitate this through appropriate policy and regulatory frameworks. Some characteristics of this ecosystem include establishing a system of property rights for quick access to financial services, eco-smart local economy-based credit rating systems, robust contract enforcement with consumer protection laws, farmer advisory services and extension services, including post-harvest processing solutions and market linkages to manage risks and deliver value addition at the farm gate.

Develop Digitally Powered Value Chain Financing

The development of digitally smart 'farm-to-fork' food value ecosystems has the potential to unlock several climate-smart solutions for the future. Governments, private corporates, civil society, academia, startups and smallholder farmer producer organisations (FPOs) should work in consortiums. By leveraging their collective internal strengths, such models can create a win-win for all stakeholders, while delivering climate goals and creating local livelihood opportunities.

The attributes of Agriculture Value Chain Financing (VCF) can be leveraged to provide holistic financial liquidity for such projects. The VCF model's efficiency can be turbocharged using digital technologies like unique identification numbers, mobile-based apps and branchless banking. It can seamlessly allow the intermingling of high-tech, scalable, personalised, collaborative precision agriculture offerings to achieve climate-smart goals. It can also be coupled with skill building and technical assistance to improve agricultural yields and reduce wastage. Such solutions can potentially bring smallholders an entire marketplace of goods and services at the click of a button in native languages.

Climate-smart agriculture financing can put into motion collaborative projects that create an impact by deploying pathbreaking innovation through rapid action. As the momentum picks up, every successful project will have a multiplier effect toward achieving a climate-resilient food ecosystem for our collective and integrated future.

How India can Galvanise PE-VC Funds for its Net-Zero Ambitions[1]

In the pursuit of a greener and more sustainable future, the world's attention has turned towards renewable energy sources as a means to mitigate climate change. However, as the climate crisis deepens, reducing the carbon footprint of electricity generation and mobility sectors is just one piece of the puzzle. In India, where the electricity sector contributes to about one-third of greenhouse gas emissions (GHG), a comprehensive energy transition demands a multi-faceted approach that goes beyond the realms of renewables and electric mobility. This realisation should entice PE-VC funds to expand their investment horizons beyond conventional sectors.

Opportunities Galore: Understanding the Decarbonisation Landscape

India's GHG emissions are a tapestry woven from various sectors like electricity (~35 per cent), agriculture (~23 per cent), manufacturing and construction (~15 per cent), transportation (~8.6 per cent), hard-to-abate industrial processes (~5 per cent), etc. Not all segments can be electrified in this intricate web to reduce GHG emissions. Each sector demands bespoke decarbonisation solutions. For instance, while the power sector aims to promote renewable energy, smart grids and long-duration grid-scale energy storage solutions, the food sector necessitates introducing precision agriculture solutions, efficient supply chain networks and organic fertilisers. The hard-to-abate industries aim to adopt novel fuels, transformative carbon-negative processes like CCUS and new raw materials for realising circular economy goals. The transportation sector looks to reinvent itself through innovations in electrification or alternate fuels like Green Hydrogen or Biofuels, smart mobility platforms and green infrastructure creation. The construction sector can cut its carbon footprint by optimising HVAC requirements, using eco-building materials and adopting green architectural design elements. Such diversity of solutions highlights the need for a holistic financing strategy that seizes decarbonisation opportunities.

[1] The article was written by Labanya Prakash Jena and Prasad Ashok Thakur and was first published by the ET Energy World (From the *Economic Times*). https://energy.economictimes.indiatimes.com/news/renewable/how-india-can-galvanize-pe-vc-funds-for-its-net-zero-ambitions/103687199

Corporate Capital and the Energy Transition Challenge

While some corporations may be able to invest significant capital, they must weigh the value of prioritising core business expansion versus energy transition initiatives. Even when the objectives of business expansion and decarbonisation overlap, they may adopt a conservative approach by staying away from investments that are perceived to be risky. Increasingly, most corporations rely on external financing for fulfilling major capex/op-ex/M&A targets, as their balance sheets might not suffice to fund ambitious projects. Herein lies the massive opportunity for PE-VC funds to spearhead India's decarbonisation journey by investing in high-potential climate solutions.

Characteristics of PE-VC Operating Arena

The climate-technology risk spectrum is typically bound by concessionary grants (high risk) at one end and conventional debt (low risk) at the other extreme. PE-VC funds have their game plays set in the middle of this spectrum. They are champions in supporting technologies that have proven viability but can present only a limited track record. Their business models can be relatively immature or untested but hold the promise of early signs of rapid scale-up potential. They are characterised by moderate risks tied to policy and regulatory uncertainty.

Climate-tech: A Perfect Opportunity to Unleash PE-VC's Strengths

So far, PE-VC funds, with their ability to provide growth capital, sector-specific expertise and risk management frameworks, emerged as a driving force behind India's ambitious clean energy projects. Fit-for-purpose climate-tech solutions for diverse sectors align remarkably well with the criteria of PE-VC investing. Such funds allow room for tailored strategies for technology enhancement and provide hands-on expert management advisory and rapid scale-up pathways with a typical time horizon of 5–7 years for producing returns. With an inherent ability to evolve as per global business cues, PE-VC funds can navigate temporary uncertainties to support innovations.

Armed with their rigorous due-diligence processes for estimating climate impact, most PE-VC funds can weed out superfluous solutions and 'greenwashing' efforts as they can set apart good investment opportunities from mere good stories. This is a much sought-after value-add towards promoting positive investor sentiments in the Indian capital ecosystem. This has contributed to broadening the active investor base (about 800 in 2022) and setting up India focused funds. Investments of PE-VC funds in India's climate-tech space are expected to mature with buyouts. The path ahead seems uncharted, but with PE-VC funds as key enablers, the transformational shift towards a greener future becomes both feasible and promising.

The Three Segments of Opportunity

The investment opportunities span electric vehicles (EVs), charging infrastructure, utility-scale energy storage and green hydrogen production. These technologies exhibit varying scales and types of investment requirements from consumer financing for EVs to substantial capital for charging stations and green hydrogen infrastructure. Within this paradigm, three distinct segments emerge as investment hotspots for private equity firms:

1. **Energy Storage:** While the technology of energy storage is established, the need for commercial capital to scale up is evident but risky for mainstream investors. PEs/VCs can invest across the value chain, including the development and deployment of advanced battery technologies and grid-scale storage solutions. The sector needs growth and risky capital to a minimal critical mass that can reduce unit cost drastically, thereby making it a profitable venture. PEs can provide this kind of capital and exit when mainstream investors are assured about the sector's profitability.
2. **Electric Vehicle Ecosystem:** The EV value chain holds tremendous potential for investment opportunity—consumer financing for personal vehicles (cars, two-wheelers, etc.), lending opportunity for commercial fleets, setting up charging networks and manufacturing of batteries and EVs.
3. **Industrial and Agricultural Decarbonisation:** Industries with intricate energy needs and emissions patterns require tailored approaches that banks and conventional financial institutions consider risky. Private equity investments will discover investment opportunities in optimising industrial processes, energy efficiency, CCUS, precision agriculture, etc.

Despite an ongoing liquidity crunch, the present interest of PE-VC funds for small to medium-sized deal activities can be just right for India's climate tech. Such funds can act as motivators for climate-tech innovators to get their unit economics right and focus on core business performance. This cautious optimism of the short term can lay the foundation for a diversified and resilient climate-solutions ecosystem in India that can serve the world's demands in achieving its net-zero ambitions.

Blended Finance: How Setting up a Financial Intermediary can Accelerate Sustainable Development[1]

With the world facing major challenges such as climate change, inequality and hunger, we need sustainable development now more than ever—but it needs adequate financing. Blended finance is the strategic use of public finance for the mobilisation of additional private finance towards sustainable development in developing countries.

The most significant value of blended finance transactions is the ability to unlock funding for investments in areas that are not well funded. These investment segments are typically seen as 'too risky' for low-risk-seeking investors, or returns are not commensurate with risk for risk-seeking investors. Despite the obvious benefits of blended finance strategies, the market for such deals has globally grown at a tepid rate. As tracked by Convergence, a global network for blended finance, since 2010, the aggregate blended finance flows touched close to $180 billion as of 2022, with annual capital flows averaging approximately $9 billion since 2015. This is significantly low considering the amount of capital required to meet sustainable development goals (SDG)—estimated at about $4.2 trillion annually in developing countries.

Challenges to Adoption of Blended Finance

Several challenges constrain the adoption of blended finance, including the small size of projects, high search, due diligence and transaction costs. In addition, private investors who may ideally be interested in investing in sustainable projects find it difficult to participate in blended finance as they may not have accessible networks, connections or the time to engage in structuring. On the other end, several small companies or projects that require the finances do not have the resources to structure deals or do not have the necessary capacity and knowledge to conduct extensive due diligence that investors need.

Multilateral development banks (MDBs) and development finance institutions (DFIs) are well-positioned to do financial intermediation to

[1] The article was written by Labanya Prakash Jena and Riya Saxena and was first published by the World Economic Forum. https://www.weforum.org/agenda/2023/04/blended-finance-financial-intermediation-can-accelerate-sustainable-development/

lead blended finance deals. However, they primarily originate blended finance deals for investing their proprietary capital; hence the potential for mobilising private capital has not been realised. This is illustrated by DFI Working Group's *Joint Reports on Blended Concessional Finance* of 2021, which suggests that MDBs deployed $1.4 billion in concessional funding, which catalysed $5.1 billion from their own account and only $3.1 billion from the private sector.

Intermediary Needed to Channel Capital Flows

The lack of an accessible intermediation platform for sustainability projects makes it hard for private financiers to participate in blended financing. Accordingly, enhancing and opening up channels where private investors can easily interact with concessional capital providers can facilitate a greater flow of capital toward the development sector. A promising solution is to build a green specialised financial intermediary, the role of which would involve:

Connecting Investors and Investees

The financial intermediary can develop its domain expertise and build a strong network in the industry to identify suitable investment opportunities for blended financing transactions. This domain knowledge and network can help the intermediary pool together various developers, companies and projects that seek debt and equity capital.

Structuring Deals to Suit the Needs of the Investors and Investees

The intermediary will also have to play the role of an aggregating agency where in investment requirements of multiple smaller companies are brought together to make a sizable investment opportunity. Feedback from investors highlights that the development community should push for deals above $500 million through aggregation platforms to unlock private capital at scale. The agency can create a place for varied types of investors—small, medium and large—to come together for investments.

The financial intermediary will also have to be familiar with the regulatory and financial landscape of the country and the international investors to develop tax-efficient structures. Over time, building standardised templates for deals rather than bespoke transactions can reduce transaction costs significantly, which will help small-size deals in particular.

Conducting Preliminary Due Diligence

Another integral value addition from the intermediary will be in conducting due diligence on at least the basic financial and legal parameters that can reduce investors' searching and transaction costs. Conducting the diligence at scale will help bring down overall transaction costs. Smaller private investors can leverage the diligence done by the intermediary to avoid duplication of resources to diligence the same investment opportunity.

Creating an Open Repository of Impact Data

Making a case for the positive 'additionality' is created by using public/philanthropic money at a lower than the market rate of return is a fundamental requirement of blended finance deals. However, often the baseline and post-project implementation impact data are either not tracked or easily available or are sitting in silos. In effect, the financial intermediary can take the lead in creating an open-source repository of detailed data on the impact of the projects. It will serve as evidence for attracting a greater flow of public capital as there would be evidence of the creation of additionality. Besides, private capital providers can better understand how this transaction structure can offer market-rate returns, thereby accelerating private capital flows.

Role of MDBs and DFIs in Blended Finance

Multilateral development banks and development finance institutions can very well continue to play the role of a financial intermediary to develop the blended finance market, but would be required to make amends to their operations and business model. This could include increasing the targets for MDBs to augment the share of private capital mobilised in blended finance transactions and making mobilisation targets a core performance indicator.

Another useful strategy would be to shift the operations of MDBs and DFIs to take positions in transactions that attract private investors rather than focus on their funds' deployment. An example of this would be the investment of MDB/DFI as second-tier capital instead of a primary capital provider in a blended finance structure. Additionally, providers of finance to the MDBs and DFIs, such as the OECD Development Assistance Committee members, can allocate greater money towards mobilising private finance. Currently, only 2 per cent of overseas development assistance is used to mobilise private capital.

How to Accelerate Blended Finance Adoption

In a nutshell, a financial intermediary can accelerate blended finance adoption to mobilise capital for sustainable development. It would need to fill in the missing gaps in the current market and is primarily responsible for coming up with new ways of attracting private capital flows to the development sector. The traditional financial institutions, the MDBs and DFIs who have done this work so far can play a major role by re-aligning themselves to pave the way for private financiers in blended finance transactions.

Climate-Tech Investments in India—Big Opportunity, Bigger Returns[1]

Reducing greenhouse gas (GHG) emissions from all sectors of the global economy is crucial to prevent hazardous climate change. Current estimates indicate that almost half of the required emissions reductions to achieve net-zero emissions by 2050 must come from technologies still in the demonstration or prototype phase. Several technologies, product design alternatives and operational methods can considerably decrease energy consumption and GHG emissions across a wide range of industries in a fast and cost-effective manner. Corporations that invest in upgraded technology will likely become leaders for the rest of the century. Investors can identify promising climate tech innovations, develop their commercial potential and deploy commercially viable climate technologies on a large scale. According to McKinsey, by 2025, next-generation climate technologies could receive $1.5 trillion to $2 trillion in capital investment annually.

Given that India is now the third-largest greenhouse gas emitter and one of the largest destinations for equity investments into startups, decarbonisation and entrepreneurship have risen to the top of the political agenda as levers to attain India's climate mitigation goals. India has a great ecosystem of startups, academia and research communities that are going full throttle on innovation in carbon-neutral/negative technologies across sectors like energy, mobility, agriculture, cement, waste management, etc. Efforts are made to tackle large-scale challenges to impact the planet while earning exponential returns positively. Investors have also recognised this momentum and are strategically making investments. During 2014–2022, about USD 2 billion were committed to climate technology. As per the Impact Investors Council (IIC) estimate, Indian Climate Tech-related startups raised USD 590 million in 2021 spread across Seed, Series A, Series B and Later Stages. The demand for climate solutions should manifest in the flow of investments for climate tech in terms of scale, speed and diversity in sectors if the target of bridging USD 1 trillion by 2030 is to be met as per the Unitus and Climake India report 2022. However, the investor community should now demonstrate more vigour.

---

[1] The article was written by Labanya Prakash Jena and Prasad Ashok Thakur and was first published by the CFA Society India. https://cfasocietyindia.org/blog/climate-tech-investments-in-india-big-opportunity-bigger-returns-cover-story/

Climate Technologies in India

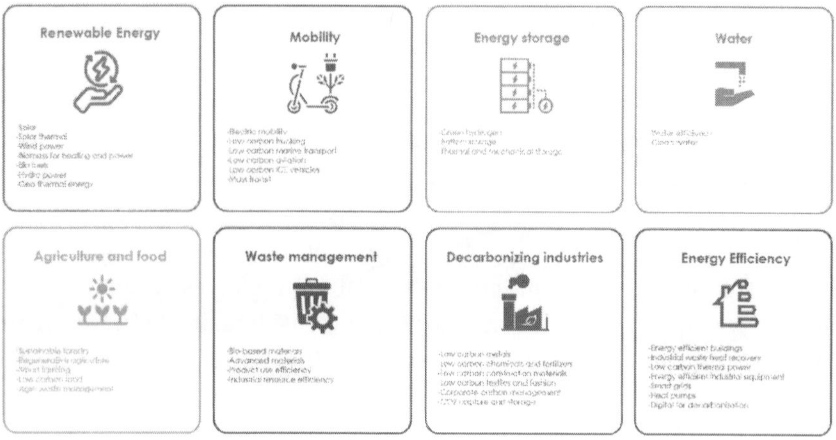

Source: https://www.eai.in/solutions/indea/ict100/2022

India: Breeding Ground for Climate-tech

India is currently home to extraordinary entrepreneurship in climate tech. The technological, financial, policy and socio-economic milieu supporting climate actions are proving to be the necessary motivator for such a revolution in the country. Simultaneously, a global mindset driving startups to 'Make in India for the world' opens up grand possibilities for sustained growth. India has all the attributes to become a thriving ground for global investors to plough their money with expectations of reaping great returns. According to an estimate, 2,260 climate tech companies based in India possess the world's third-largest cluster of firms working towards mitigating climate change, lagging behind the United States (7,561) and the United Kingdom (2,503).

However, it is observed that investors need more convincing with business models when it comes to obtaining 'assured returns' from a long-term perspective. Currently, only the renewable energy generation like solar and wind and electric vehicle sectors have been somewhat successful in attracting sizeable commitments from the investor community. However, there are ample investment opportunities across the sectors and stages.

Investment Momentum is Across Sectors

India needs investments spread over a diverse portfolio of climate technologies to create a meaningful impact on its people, planet and business profits. As per the 'State of Climate Finance in India' report, sustainable food value chains in the country may require investments to the tune of USD 300 billion by

2030. Similarly, Water and Solid Waste Management needs approximately USD 200 billion and demand side management of energy has an investment potential of about USD 60 billion. Similar quantum of investment is required for interdisciplinary sectors like deep tech for meteorological models, circular economy-based supply chains, nature-based solutions, people-skilling for green jobs, etc. The PE-VC community must realise that these are evolving opportunities redefining human entrepreneurship's frontiers. These sectors may trace investment and return patterns that may differ significantly from conventional assets. Many startups in this space may not have financial track records, thus making their valuations tricky. However, several policy initiatives have shown that the macro-trends are decisively shifting in favour of giving precedence to environmental sustainability at par with business sustainability. Some recent examples are Electricity Amendment Act, Energy Conservation Act, Green Hydrogen Policy, National Policy on Biofuels, etc. This is mobilising the climate-tech startup community towards better predictability in their revenue models while improving their product-market-environment fitment. This phenomenon should act as a guiding light for the investment community toward committing to investments beyond the early stages of climate tech.

Climate Smart Investing: Access to New Wealth

As India boasts of one of the world's youngest populations, its appetite for environmentally sustainable products and services is increasing. Such choices also influence the investment decisions of its young demography. As per a study by Morgan Stanley, most millennials are inclined towards investing in companies or funds that rate highly on social and environmental deliverables while generating comparable market returns. This trend emerges from a realisation that their investment decisions can make a difference in the fight against climate change. As observed in the developed world, this is an irreversible trend. As wealth gets generated and transferred across generations that are progressively better off than the previous generations in meeting their basic requirements, the opportunities and willingness to invest in climate tech are expected to grow exponentially. It makes sense for PE-VC funds, institutional investors and HNIs to generate and scout for such opportunities to match these evolving tastes and preferences of the new age.

Undoubtedly, the world is confronting an unprecedented climate change crisis and climate technologies are set to assume a pivotal function in addressing these issues. Climate tech investors will be crucial in making these solutions feasible, and on the way, they will generate wealth as well.

Is India's Equity Market Responding to the Threat of Climate Change?[1]

The Financial Sector is Exposed to Climate Change Risk

Climate change is threatening economic growth, food production, livelihood and the financial system. In the 'Report on Trend and Progress of Banking in India,' Reserve Bank of India (RBI) acknowledged that climate change risks could adversely affect the stability of the financial system. As climate change risk is recognised as a systemic risk to financial stability and potentially affect the performance of the portfolio exposed significantly to carbon emitting and polluting sectors, there is an urgent need to change portfolio allocation.

Climate change risk is going to adversely affect more to long term institutional investors like insurance companies and pension funds compared to short/medium term investors since both liability duration of these investors and realisation of climate change are long. Climate change risk is more problematic for the insurance company since their liability is linked to the adverse impact of climate change. An increase in the frequency of natural disasters such as floods and storms increases the insurance claims and, consequently, growing liability for insurance companies. For example, total global losses due to weather catastrophes were $340 bn in 2017 due to weather catastrophes, out of which $138 bn were insured losses[1]. Indian banks and investors have an exposure of $1.4 tn[2] to sectors that are prone to climate change risk—both physical and transition risks. In this scenario, the government is expected to come out with policy regulation favourable to carbon mitigating economic activities and penalising carbon-emitting businesses. Hence, the expected change in policy and regulation warrants the rebalancing of the banks and institutional investors' portfolios and calls for a shift in their asset allocation in favour of green businesses.

---

1 The article was written by Labanya Prakash Jena was first published by the CFA Society India. https://cfasocietyindia.org/blog/is-indias-equity-market-responding-to-the-threat-of-climate-change/

Interrelationships between the Financial Sector, Real Sector and Climate Change

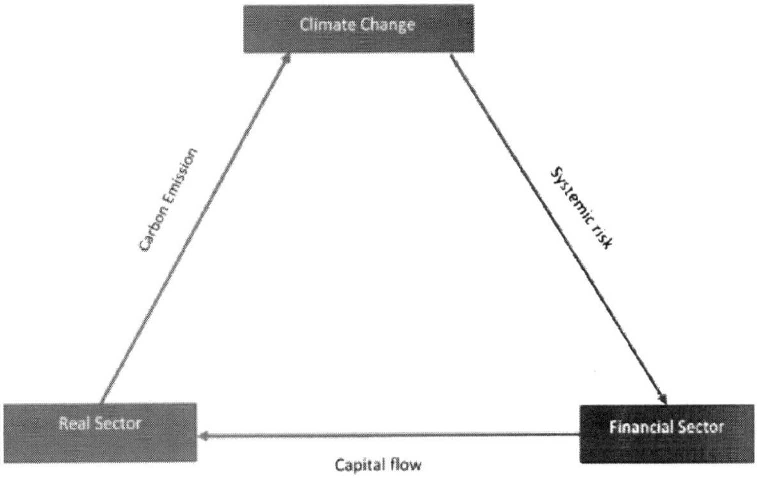

Source: Author's Analysis

Does India's stock market react to climate change risk?

Source: BSE Database

Note: The S&P BSE Greenex is designed to measure the performance of the top 25 'green' companies in terms of greenhouse gas (GHG) emissions, market cap and liquidity.

The above chart suggests that the 'green' index has underperformed than the market index (BSE Sensex) over 2010–2019. The 'green' index lagged the market, particularly after 2017, when India has come out with several measures to decarbonise the economy and made a commitment at the Paris Agreement to reduce carbon emission intensity of GDP by 33 per cent to 35 per cent. Logically, the green companies should have performed better than the market since the government is expected to deploy policy and regulatory measures to incentivise 'green' companies and penalise the carbon-emitting companies. However, the above chart indicates that the Indian stock market has not captured environmental risks yet. The market efficiency theory suggests that market participants incorporate all the information in capital allocation, which reflected in the market price. However, sometimes market participants don't have enough useful information to decide or do not know how to interpret available information. In the long term, the market will be more efficient as the companies start disclosing more information on climate risk and opportunity (either forced by regulator or investors or other stakeholders). Besides, market participants will be paying more attention as the impact of climate change become more visible and learn ways to interpret this material, climate change risk and opportunity, information.

Our primary research with institutional investors indicates that insurance, pension and mutual funds are not focused on environmental risk. The financial market regulators such as PFRDA, IRDA and SEBI have not paid attention yet on climate change risk in their regulatory guidelines. PFRDA and IRDA can make climate change risk assessment of portfolio as a fiduciary responsibility of fund managers, which can force them to incorporate this imminent risk in their investment decision making. SEBI can recognise climate change risk and opportunity as material information and make regulation on compulsory disclosure of climate change risk disclosure of listed companies, which can help investors in making an informed decision on securities and sector selection. It is noteworthy here that oversight of climate change risk exposes the financial sector to systemic climate change risk.

The Way Forward: Need to Allocate Capital to Mitigate Climate Change Risk

Since the carbon-intensive sectors are currently facing both physical and transition risk, consequently eroding the profitability of these sectors and companies who are exposed to these risks. Hence, the investors should identify companies who are proactive in taking the right steps in mitigating these risks. Besides, the investors should look at investment opportunities in the sectors which are climate-friendly, such as clean energy, energy-efficient and clean transportation, to mitigate climate change risk.

Sources

[1] https://www.munichre.com/content/dam/assets/munichre/content-pieces/documents/pdf/302-09092_en.pdf

[2] http://www.emergingmarketsdialogue.org/wp-content/uploads/2018/04/Study-Natural-Capital-Risk-Exposure-of-the-Financial-Sector-in-India.pdf

Climate-related Financial Risk: Making a Truly Transformational Change in Investment Strategy[1]

Climate change is an inevitable threat to global and local economies and markets if proper and urgent steps are not taken to mitigate these risks. There is academic evidence that climate change, in the form of transition and physical risks, is adversely affecting financial assets. Since climate change is affecting capital flows and the cost of capital, the corporates are expected to vigorously take both adaption and mitigation measures to control, shift and manage these risks. On the other hand, the financers, particularly large ones such as banks and institutional investors, are considering these risks in securities selection and portfolio construction.

In the last few years, large financial institutions have invested heavily in capacity building, including skilling manpower, developing new technologies and tools and creating databases to better understand these risks. The early movers can enjoy the competitive advantage not only in identifying and better managing these risks but also in harnessing the opportunities emanating from climate change. The financial policies of these financial institutions are different from traditional securities selection and portfolio construction. They are redefining their investment strategy—setting new rules and changing procedures—to select securities and design investment portfolios, manage risks and create a compensation structure. In this article, I have outlined the best practices that will make true transformational changes in investment management concerning climate change.

Set a Minimum Standard

Positive or negative screening is the easiest way of selecting securities. Negative screening involves exclusion of certain industries from her investment universe that are more vulnerable to climate change risks or excluding securities with low ESG or carbon ratings. Positive screening involves selecting industries that will benefit from climate change or include only best-in-class securities based on ESG or carbon rating. These two ways

[1] The article was written by Labanya Prakash Jena and was first published by the CFA Society India. https://cfasocietyindia.org/blog/climate-related-financial-risk-making-a-truly-transformational-change-in-investment-strategy/

may not be the efficient way of securities selection as they exclude a vast number of industries and securities from the investment universe. Besides, ESG rating is also not fully proven as the best way for securities selection from a climate change perspective since there is a divergence in ESG rating among various rating agencies. This means the investment house can create an in-house and robust methodology to assess climate change risks and opportunities in the value-creation chain on the corporate's sustainable profitability and valuation. The methodology can identify securities based on quantitative data (e.g., carbon intensity, energy efficiency, resource efficiency, water management, etc.) and judgment (e.g., the company's strategy and vision concerning climate change). The quantitative data and judgment can be converted into scores that can decide buy, hold or sell securities from the perspective of climate change.

Set a New Benchmark

Benchmark is like a gold standard for the fund managers—they always want to beat or at least meet the benchmark without deviating from its risk exposure. However, traditional market indexes are built on historical performance without regard for climate change that will be materialised in the future. This warrants the replacement of traditional benchmarks with a new benchmark that captures climate change risks and opportunities.

Invest in Climate-risk Modelling

The traditional risk management tools such as back-testing are not relevant as climate-related risks are going to be materialised in the future. Hence, fund houses are developing climate-risk modelling in-house or relying on third parties to develop new tools to assess climate risks. However, climate-risk modelling in the financial sector is at a nascent stage and evolving rapidly. So, the available models and databases need to upgrade constantly. The fund house should build in-house capabilities for climate-risk modelling while working with third-party agencies supplying useful data and tools. The fund house should hire climate scientists, catastrophic modelers and climate finance/policy specialists who can together design in-house climate-risk modelling.

Develop Manpower Capacity

Fund houses are heavily investing in developing the technical capacity of staff to better assess climate risks and opportunities. These knowledge gaps may lead to an underestimation of climate change risk or overlooking opportunities in lending and investments. The fund houses can encourage or invest their investment professionals to gain knowledge and expertise in climate change. The fund houses can design specific training for their staff across all levels to better understand the risk. 'Certificate in ESG Investing' offered by the CFA Institute and 'Sustainability and Climate Risk' certification programme by the Global Association of Risk Professionals (GARP) are some good distance learning programmes for practitioners.

Align Compensation Structure with Climate Target

The existing compensation structure of most fund houses is based on the fund manager's portfolio performance that may not capture climate change risk and opportunities appropriately. The fund house can design the compensation structure based on the combined investment performances and climate resilience of the portfolio. For example, the fund house may set a target for a net-zero portfolio by a specific year with an intermediate target every year.

Set New Rules

The traditional rules on the market, sector, industry or target weightings and risk measures need to be revisited. Most of these rules are based on historical performance records that do not capture climate change risk. For example, back-testing, a traditional risk management measure, is not very helpful since most climate-related risks are expected to be materialised in the future and differ. Besides, traditional rules may stifle innovations that are required to address climate change risks and opportunities that have not been realised earlier.

Any transformation changes in investment strategy and portfolio construction need to break existing rules and behavioural barriers and adapt new hypotheses and modify behaviour to new dynamics. Climate change is a transformation event in human history and potentially hampers financial asset value significantly and/or suddenly. This new event warrants a radical change in investment practices. Implementing these originative changes in investment practices requires leadership and intensive dialogue with the asset owners to make the portfolio resilient against this eminent risk and harness the opportunities.

Cut Carbon Emissions with Transition Financing[1]

Does the world want to go green in all sectors? Most likely. But this goal faces a key complexity—how do you enable transition polluting industries and help them reduce emissions? This is where innovative financing solutions can play a role. Take the case of India. It is on a trajectory to decarbonise its economy, fulfil its Nationally Determined Contributions (NDCs) commitment and achieve sustainable development goals. In relative terms, India's industrial emissions per unit of gross value added is twice that of G20 countries—reflecting the country's emissions-intensive fuel/energy usage. As India's economy grows, the demand for various carbon-intensive commodities—such as steel, cement and chemicals—is likely to grow by at least three-fold between 2014 and 2030. The current low levels of per capita resource consumption in India are also moving towards the global average, with the increase in per capita income.

The energy sector accounts for 67 per cent of India's greenhouse gas (GHG) emissions, followed by the industrial sector (20 per cent) and the agriculture and land-use sectors (13 per cent). Within the energy sector, industries are the highest consumer of electricity, accounting for 42 per cent. In total, the industrial sector and so-called 'polluting industries' account for around 48 per cent of the total GHG emission in India.

Investment Dilemma

While there is a need to focus on 'polluting industries', many of them are asset-heavy in nature. There is a large sunk cost in the existing facilities and the complexity of operations. As a result, the investment cycles are incredibly long—companies in these industries change their facilities and operation only gradually over the years. These industries typically have significant long-term financing needs to reduce their GHG emissions. But alarmingly, these industries are not investing in decarbonisation technologies at the expected levels. Why so?

---

[1] The article was written by Labanya Prakash Jena and was first published by the *Hindu Business Line*. https://www.thehindubusinessline.com/opinion/cut-carbon-emissions-with-transition-financing/article33447241.ece

One reason is that while the market for decarbonisation (including energy efficiency) appears to be very large, it has only seen limited dedicated investment options. Traditional forms of sustainable/green finance do not cover these. Take the case of green bonds—they are designed for green industries only. For example, a coal power company cannot issue green bonds to finance its supercritical plants or decommission old power plants. This is despite the fact that both those activities could reduce GHG emissions.

This is where transition finance can step in. Transition finance allows polluting industries to attract capital to transform into low-GHG-intensive businesses, but not necessarily become totally green. This enables firms that would not qualify to issue green bonds to obtain sustainability-related financing.

It also helps these industries raise long-term capital to become less carbon-intensive in the long-term. The fund usage is more flexible compared to green finance and creates more investment and decarbonisation options.

So how does it work? Companies can raise capital at a corporate level and utilise it to optimise profitability and reduction of carbon emission. The financers can set certain terms and conditions, particularly to link financing to specific outcomes, for the corporates to create accountability and transparency. A third-party verifier can be appointed to verify the company's GHG emissions target.

One example is the $350-million transition bond issued in 2020 by the Hong Kong-based Castle Peak Power Company. The funds were used to construct an offshore LNG receiving terminal and other supporting assets, to move away from a coal power plant to a less carbon-intensive natural gas power plant. Similarly, the Brazil-based meat production company Marfrig issued a transition bond in 2019 to practice sustainable cattle ranching—ensuring that cattle farmers do not encroach the Amazon rainforest.

Some Caveats

Like green bonds—accused of 'greenwashing'—transition financing also draws criticism from environmental groups. There are fears that polluting companies will issue these bonds to mitigate their reputational risks but will continue with their carbon-emitting operations without taking concrete actions to reduce pollution.

However, financial companies are developing guidelines for transition financing which can alleviate these concerns. Third-party verifying agencies can also play an important role here, in ensuring that the proceeds are indeed used for decarbonising operations.

With the right principles, financial incentives for issuers and clear key performance indicators, transition financing can play a powerful role in decarbonising India's polluting industries and help India to meet its NDCs and sustainability goals.

How can Family-managed Businesses Save the Earth from Climate Change?[1]

Climate change poses a tangible and imminent threat that can jeopardise the economy, businesses and the financial system. It is already acknowledged as a systemic risk to financial stability. Climate-related physical risks, such as hurricanes, floods, sea level rise, heat waves and precipitation, have the potential to directly cause harm to assets or disrupt companies' value chains. Similarly, climate-related transition risks emerge from the shift to a low-carbon economy through changes in policy and technology, which can undermine the performance of greenhouse gas (GHG) emitting industries. However, corporate efforts to mitigate climate change risks currently lack confidence, posing not only a threat to the economy but also to corporations themselves.

Corporate Governance Structure is a Key Barrier

In modern enterprises, most of the key decision-making is in the hands of professional managers (agents), who are hired by shareholders/owners (principals) to effectively perform activities in the best interests of principals. However, the contract between the principal and agent does not give agents significant incentives to make the business climate-sensitive—not investing adequately in low-carbon technologies or mitigating climate-related business risks. Creative risk-taking for long-term value creation may also not be rewarded. The incentive structure exerts pressure on agents to increase the company's short-term earnings, which may not necessarily align with the country's green economic transition and also exposes the company to climate-related risk. A large chunk of the manager's compensation in the form of a bonus is tied to the profitability and stock price of the firm—many times, the stock market doesn't reward managers for taking steps to mitigate climate change risk or penalise them for not taking enough measures to mitigate climate change risks. The compensation structure encourages managers to save money in the short term, even if it compromises actions to mitigate climate change risks and leverage green opportunities. All these factors help

[1] The article was written by Labanya Prakash Jena and Prasad Ashok Thakur and was first published by the Illuminem. https://illuminem.com/illuminemvoices/how-can-familymanaged-businesses-save-the-earth-from-climate-change

the firm show reduced costs, increase in profitability and consequently, stock price in the short term only.

The Family Business Structure is Designed for Playing the Long-term Game

Family businesses (FBs) constitute a significant segment of today's global corporate environment. According to a report from PricewaterhouseCoopers, FBs represent approximately 80 per cent of the engineering and construction sectors, 55 per cent of the automotive sector and 33 per cent of the retail clothing sectors. Additionally, industries such as shipping, banking and capital markets, insurance, metals and mining are also heavily influenced by sizable FBs. Research conducted by the Boston Consulting Group indicates that around 30 per cent of large companies in advanced economies are FBs, with this figure rising to about 60 per cent in developing nations. Notably, FBs are renowned for their emphasis on resilience and long-term strategic planning, attributes that position them as potential allies in climate action endeavours.

Family Businesses are Well-positioned to Tackle Climate change Challenges While Generating Long-term Sustainable Value

Family firms tend to have permanent owners. Long-term orientation is a common trait of FBs. FBs encourage decision-making to prioritise sustainable value instead of generating only short-term profits. Family firms not only influence the strategic decision-making of their affiliates but also can nudge policymakers for a green economic transition which can be a win-win proposition for the entire economy and themselves. Corporate chronicles illustrate that family managed companies have helped economic development in late-industrialising economies and they transformed and evolved with the change in time in these economies. As they are primed to think more long term, they may not be under compulsions to please the whims and fancies of the analysts for every quarter. Moreover, as the cumulative wisdom of successfully running the business passes from one generation to the other, members of the promoter/owner family may make decisions that will allow them to create value in the long term.

Parallelly, climate change or environmental issues were previously considered purely from an ethics-based lens. However, in the present times, they are at the very core of mainstream business strategies for generating sustainable value for shareholders. Interpreting such evolving trends in an integrated manner may work in favour of certain climate solutions that are proven, but do not yet have a track record to show for raising finances from financial institutions. In such cases, climate entrepreneurs can pitch their business propositions to an array of relevant FBs to find a perfect match for their growth partnerships. On the flip side, the fresh perspectives and dynamism from the global net-zero landscape brought in by climate entrepreneurs can be leveraged by FBs as their competitive advantage.

Family businesses can become climate action torchbearers for the corporate world. They can establish novel incentive systems for their employees and partners to aim for sustainability, seizing long-term, environmentally friendly business opportunities. This will foster goodwill and partnerships, collectively mitigating climate change-induced disruptions.

Mobilising Green Finance for Indian MSMEs[1]

India has 63 million Micro, Small and Medium Enterprises (MSMEs), the second-highest number in the world after China. MSMEs contribute around 30 per cent of India's Gross Domestic Product (GDP), 40 per cent of its exports and employ about 110 million people. In addition, MSMEs' energy consumption is equivalent to 20–25 per cent of the energy consumed by India's large industries sector. Yet despite their economic significance and their role in India reaching net-zero emissions by 2070, MSMEs are unable to secure the financing they need to decarbonise.

Energy costs for the most polluting MSMEs in the manufacturing sector are 10–30 per cent of total production costs, which creates an obvious incentive to invest in energy-efficient plants and machinery and source electricity from cheaper renewable sources. However, MSMEs lack the capacity and financial resources to do this. The barriers to accessing commercially available finance include stiff lending policies with high collateral security requirements, small project ticket sizes and high transaction costs. And without an investment-grade credit rating or a strong Environmental, Social and Governance (ESG) profile, MSMEs are also unable to access the trillion-dollar sustainable debt market. In the absence of immediate viable financial solutions, MSMEs need government intervention to get sustainable debt at a reasonable rate. A way forward could be a green finance platform for MSMEs.

Green Finance Platform for MSMEs

A green finance platform could help MSMEs access green bond capital. An appropriate institution would govern the platform, issuing green bonds and disbursing the proceeds to MSMEs via green loans. It would develop criteria for an eligible MSME green borrower based on its environmental profile and business activity or project to mitigate the environmental impact. Alternatively, the governing institution could loan the proceeds of green bonds to financial institutions that would then on-lend to eligible MSMEs.

[1] The article was written by Labanya Prakash Jena and Saurabh Trivedi and was published by Institute for Energy Economics and Financial Analysis. https://ieefa.org/resources/how-mobilise-green-finance-indian-micro-small-and-medium-enterprises

The green loans could be term loans, revolving credit facilities or other debt instruments.

The platform would adhere to the Securities and Exchange Board of India's disclosure requirements for bond issuance and the Loan Market Association's Green Loan Principles (GLP) for green loans. The bond issuer would ensure regular impact reporting to investors based on the International Capital Market Association's guidelines by working closely with MSMEs on each project. It would also appoint a third-party verification agency to ensure loan proceeds fund green projects.

The governing institution would therefore need to be an entity with a high credit rating, have experience in bond issuance, a working relationship with the MSME sector, a strong balance sheet and an understanding of the impact of climate risk on financial performance.

The Small Industrial Development Bank of India (SIDBI) meets these criteria.

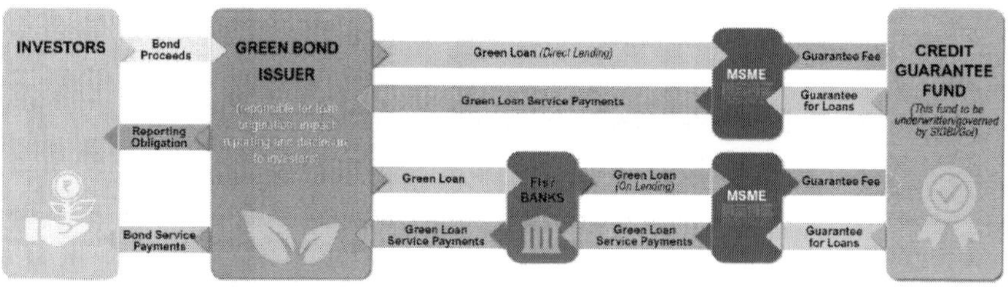

SIDBI in Ideal Position to Govern Green Finance Platform

SIDBI could govern the green finance platform, especially given its mandate to oversee MSMEs. SIDBI, backed by the Government of India (GoI), has a strong AAA (ICRA) credit rating. It is also an accredited entity of the Green Climate Fund (GCF), demonstrating its ability to understand climate change business dynamics. While not currently issuing green bonds, SIDBI could follow multilateral development institutions and other GoI-backed Indian institutions, like Indian Renewable Energy Development Agency and Rural Electrification Corporation Limited, which have successfully issued green bonds worth more than US$1 trillion as at September 2022.

Barriers Addressed Through this Platform

If SIDBI were to become the governing institution of such a green finance platform, it would help address a number of barriers MSMEs face in accessing the finance they need to decarbonise. First, the proposed structure would overcome the MSMEs' poor credit profile because of SIDBI's strong credit rating. Second, it would ensure that the green bond issue size is adequate, which is unlikely if MSMEs raise such bonds individually. Third, with adequate policy or financial support for MSMEs from the GoI/SIDBI, the interest rates on these loans would be relatively low and could attract longer tenors. Finally, a strong issuer like SIDBI would attract ESG investors looking to generate a significant impact on their investment.

Challenges and Solutions

Still, there are challenges to adopting such a structure that would need to be addressed. MSMEs' poor credit profile could impact the rating of the proposed SIDBI green bond making it too risky for investors and increase subsequent green loan interest costs. To mitigate these risks, the GoI could design a credit guarantee fund to finance green projects for MSMEs similar to the existing Credit Guarantee Fund Trust for Micro and Small Enterprises (CGTMSE).

The proposed guarantee fund would absorb the potential default risk of MSMEs while ensuring the availability of collateral-free green loans for MSMEs. Similar to CGTMSE, the new guarantee fund should provide cover to green loans for up to 85 per cent of the loan value, which SIDBI and GoI should underwrite.

MSME borrowers may also lack the capacity to adhere to GLP guidelines. SIDBI would need to conduct capacity-building exercises for MSME borrowers to ensure they adhere to GLP. A small technical assistance pool, funded by public institutions, would be required to cover the technical assistance costs, including capacity building and third-party verification costs. As an accredited GCF entity, SIDBI could use the GCF's technical assistance grant for eligible projects.

Benefits for SIDBI

SIDBI has much to gain from the proposed green financing platform. It would unlock green capital for SIDBI, which it has not explored yet, especially through capital markets. It can enhance its reputation among ESG investors. As financial institutions come under increasing scrutiny on their climate risk management, green bond issuance by SIDBI would send a positive signal about its intent on climate action. The platform would also enhance SIDBI's role as a development institution by adding climate-related funding as a goal to its mandate of protecting and accelerating MSMEs to meet its socio-economic development goals.

Currently, India has no dedicated platform to finance the decarbonisation of MSMEs. SIDBI could fill this gap and mobilise green bond capital for Indian MSMEs through the proposed mechanism.

We Need to Decarbonise Industry: Here's How to Finance It[1]

The 2015 Paris Agreement recognises that keeping the increase in global average temperature below 2°C from pre-industrial levels would significantly reduce the impact of climate change. In order to achieve this, it will be essential to decarbonise industry. Direct industrial processes contribute 5.2 per cent of global greenhouse gas emissions, while energy use in industries contributes about 24.2 per cent. This is set to rise further with rapid industrialisation and the use of emission-intensive processes, particularly in developing countries.

There are many ways of reducing emissions in industry. For example, some state-of-the-art industrial technologies can absorb carbon dioxide through 'carbon scrubbing'. Industries can introduce circular economy principles in production and supply chain and use sustainable alternative fuels. Some estimates indicate that replacing existing assets or processes in heavy industries could reduce carbon emissions by 10-20 per cent without any significant adverse impact on financial returns.

However, it is currently very difficult for businesses to adopt low carbon and energy-efficient technologies, due to a lack of suitable financing. There are huge costs involved in constructing new project facilities and buying specialised equipment, especially for heavy industries like chemical, steel and cement. Businesses do not plan to replace these kind of assets frequently and upgrading them or replacing them requires substantial investment. It can also be difficult to salvage equipment once it has been decommissioned.

In order to change their assets and systems, project owners need to see financial benefits. There are currently few market-tested mechanisms to price industrial carbon emissions, which means that there is little incentive for businesses to shut down higher carbon-emitting legacy production plants, machinery and processes, or to replace them with capital-intensive, low carbon-intensive technologies.

1 The article was written by Labanya Prakash Jena and Shreyansh Jain and was first published by the World Economic Forum. https://www.weforum.org/agenda/2022/01/financial-innovation-to-decarbonize-the-industrial-sector/

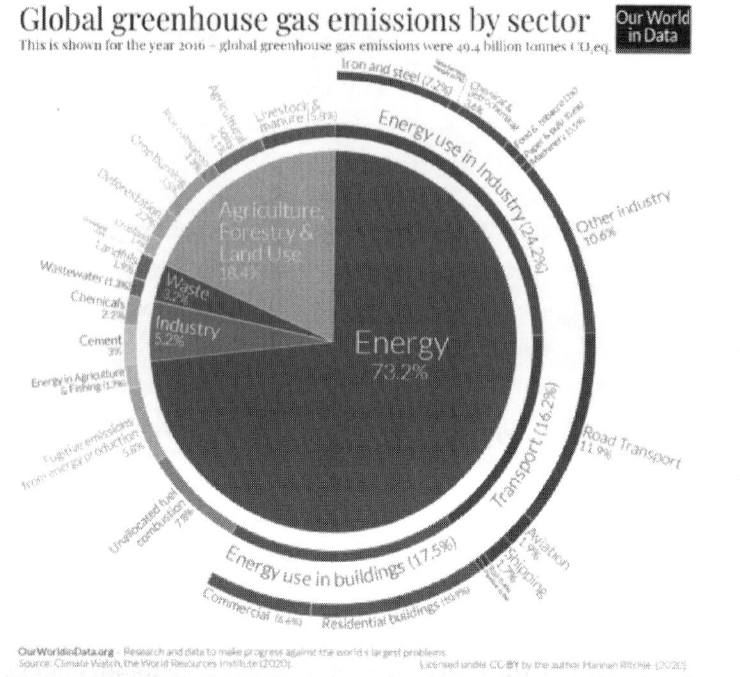

Direct industrial processes contribute 5.2 per cent of global greenhouse gas emissions, while energy use in industries contributes about 24.2 per cent.

Image: Our World in Data

Debt financers, particularly banks, do not consider energy-efficient industrial equipment as an attractive lending proposition. There is a lack of credible historical data on the energy efficiency of new equipment and a perceived risk of the equipment failing to yield adequate financial savings. Once any new equipment is integrated with the project facility, it is also difficult for the lender to separate and ring-fence the asset in order to use it as collateral on the loan. If the borrower defaults, the debt financer might be left with a stranded asset that is not easy to liquidate in the secondary marketplace.

Often, businesses that wish to adopt new technology to reduce emissions are left with Hobson's choice: either issue fresh equity or raise debt from capital markets. The former leads to a lower return on equity in the near term. The latter is not efficient either, as debt providers demand a higher coupon rate and stringent covenants to make sure that proceeds are used for their intended purpose.

If we want industry to decarbonise, we need to make debt capital available at a cost that does not discourage lenders or lower the business's return on equity. This could be done with public-funded unsecured subordinated debt financing. This is a debt that takes second place to other debts when it comes to claims on assets.

It would provide reassurance to debt financers and to sweeten the deal for the creditor, the subordinated debt could be offered as a payment-in-kind note, deferring regular principal and interest payments until the financial benefits of the new technology have been realised. The tenor of the subordinated debt could also be longer than those of existing debts, offering extra security to existing debt financers.

This would help the borrower to develop an improved credit profile, discouraging existing debt financers from imposing stringent covenants on their debt. Furthermore, as the business is not required to issue fresh equity to raise funds, the new debt would not affect the return for existing capital providers. The business can mobilise additional resources at a relatively low cost, without reducing the equity holdings of existing shareholders. Lastly, during the repayment period, the borrower would be eligible to claim a tax deduction on the interest paid on subordinated debt.

The source of public finance for this subordinated debt financing could be a line of credit from multilateral development banks, international financing mechanisms like Green Climate Fund, public financial institutions, governments, or green bonds issued by the borrower to one of these institutions.

It would be possible to identify standardised plants, equipment and processes that reduce carbon emissions substantially and offer financial benefits, rather than backing a variety of technologies across industrial sectors. The initial identification of standardised technologies would help to reduce the costs of researching and assessing the environmental and financial benefits of new technologies. At the COP26 Summit in Glasgow, several countries committed to achieving net-zero carbon emissions by mid-century. Increased uptake of low-carbon equipment in the industrial sector will play an important role in the rapid decarbonisation course.

Sustainability and Indian Banking System: A Perspective and Way Forward[1]

The structural transformation of India's economy towards sustainability requires large-scale capital; the banking system plays an important role in funding the transition. Its role becomes important in India, where debt capital is mostly routed through banks instead of the capital market. Particularly, medium and small-sized companies (MSMEs) rely on bank financing for their CAPEX and OPEX funding needs. As banks finance through corporate and project financing routes, sustainable[2] businesses or technologies can raise capital from banks instead of the capital market in the most efficient way.

Globally, several banks have declared to become 'net-zero' financers by 2050—it means their lending, operation and advisory businesses directly or indirectly will not emit any carbon on a net basis. However, only one India bank, HDFC Bank, has declared any such ambition even if the Government of India has announced to reach net-zero by 2070. Only a single bank signed the Principle of Responsible Banking (PRB), an initiative by the United Nations Environment Programme Finance Initiative (UNEP FI). HDFC Bank announced to become net-zero by 2030, but that is only restricted in the bank's operation, not in their lending portfolio. Since banks' direct carbon emission is trivial compared to their lending portfolio—their borrowers in the real economy emit carbon. So, banks' declaration to reach net-zero in their operation will neither help the climate change actions nor make their business resilient against climate change risk. It is another matter that global banks currently have huge carbon-emitting business exposure and the net-zero target in 2040 and beyond is a long way to go. The declaration could be lip service to shield the wrath from the civil societies and market.

Banking Supervisors Do Not Consider Sustainability Risk

Banks mostly consider sustainability risk at the individual transaction level (Basel Pillar 1)—whether any laws or regulations are violated or will be possibly violated, which can hamper the project's cash flow generation.

---

1 The article was written by Labanya Prakash Jena and was first published by the CFA Society India. https://cfasocietyindia.org/blog/cover-story-sustainability-and-indian-banking-system-a-perspective-and-way-forward/

2 I am using sustainability and climate change interchangeably in this article

However, banks' existing sustainable risk assessment is mostly related to meeting government regulation or community challenges rather than the material risk beyond government regulation—which can jeopardise the project's commercial viability. The incorporation of sustainability risk is missing at Basel Pillar II and III. The banking supervisor in India (RBI) does not consider climate change risk when assessing the overall risk of the banks (Issue Pillar II), and banks do not disclose climate change risk to the market (Pillar III). The current regulation does not cover climate change risk in Pillar II and Pillar III.

Sustainability is Missing in the Strategy and Governance of Banks

Banks have short or medium-term asset and liability duration, unlike institutional investors. They do not consider climate change a material risk in the business operation as they are likely to materialise longer. As the risk is long-term, it is not captured in the bank's business planning and lending operation—a phenomenon Former Governor of England said is a 'Tragedy of the Horizon.' Another issue is related to the engagement of the board of directors and top leadership on climate change. Expertise on financial risk related to climate change is missing at the board and top leadership level, which reflects from Indian bank's absence in various climate change initiatives and limited disclosure on banks' strategy or plan in regulatory reports.

Banks Cannot Ignore Climate Change Risk

Let's assume banks for a second, climate change will not affect banks' lending portfolio as they are short to medium term (max seven years) while climate change risk will significantly affect in the long term (after ten years). If banks assume this, it is risky because climate change-related events are becoming more severe and frequent every year, e.g., floods in Mumbai and cyclones in eastern and southern India. There is also a tail risk associated with climate change, which may hit the lending portfolio at any time.

Banks also face climate risk on the market side. As banks are currently listed in the foreign stock market (e.g., NYSE, LSE), investors in the foreign market have started considering climate change risk in their investment decision-making. Banks' significant exposure to carbon-emitting sectors may face the ire of these investors if banks do not incorporate climate change in business planning and lending operation. Similarly, Indian banks also raise debt capital from the foreign market; the cost of debt financing may be higher for banks having substantial loan exposure to carbon-emitting businesses.

Indian banks, as listed in India, do not have to disclose climate-related risk as extensively as international standards (TCFD, for example). There is a possibility they may be forced to follow TCFD for being listed in these stock exchanges as several financial regulators are considering TCFD as a compulsory disclosure standard for listed companies and bond issuers. Indian banks' heavy exposure to carbon-emitting businesses and lack of intent to decarbonise their lending portfolio may suddenly become a huge market risk in the foreign market and transmitted to the Indian stock market. Any sharp decrease in stock price will consequently affect the cost of funding of banks. The mandatory adoption of BRSR could be a good beginning for banks to gradually move to the International disclosure standard. Still, BRSR is more of stock-taking rather than forward-looking, which is more meaningful considering climate change is going to the businesses in the future.

Way Forward

Of course, banks will do start integrating climate change in their governance, strategy, planning, disclosure and risk management practices as the regulatory and reputation pressure are mounting. I am focussing on the banks' lending operations. There are three approaches banks can follow: a. Exclusion of carbon-emitting sectors/companies; b. Integration of climate change in loan pricing; c. Engagement with corporates.

Exclusion

Banks can stop lending or refinance heavily carbon-emitting or polluting industries/companies. However, this step can help banks reduce climate-related transition risks in their lending portfolio, but not completely. The interlink of companies/industries and climate-related physical risks (acute and chronic risk) will still expose banks to climate change risk. It is not a smart approach for banks as they may lose a large lending portfolio, interest income and advisory services related to these companies/industries. As some carbon-emitting companies or industries have significant constituents of the economy, they are the largest customers of banks. Banks cannot afford to lose these high-value customers. Besides, several conglomerates, mostly in debt-heavy capital-intensive businesses, denying loans to a single entity may prompt the conglomerate to switch to alternative banks. Banks will lose both fee-based and fund-based income from these conglomerates.

Integration of Climate Change in Loan Pricing

Banks can absorb climate change risk in calculating loan risk premiums. Banks can charge higher interest rates on loans borrowers exposed to climate change risk and lower interest rates on climate-friendly borrowers. For example, the interest rate can be determined by carbon performance; for example, carbon rating, GHG/Revenue compared to the peers or historically, etc. This incentive mechanism will encourage corporates to decarbonise their business to reduce interest costs.

The key challenge is identifying the material risk factors that differ across companies or industries. Even if banks identify these factors, borrowers are not disclosing enough to measure the exposure and intensity of these risks, which makes it impossible to price these risks appropriately. The disclosure through the BRSR framework should help up to a greater extent. Banks can ask their borrowers to disclose climate-related materials risk factors during the lending assessment process.

Since there is a great distrust among investors and lenders on ESG scoring, banks can develop an internal carbon credit model to calculate credit risks based on companies' disclosure. Banks can use sophisticated models developed by various institutions and technology companies to identify risks of different industries and companies and assess these risks more correctly, thereby improving banks' lending processes.

Engagement with Corporates

Unlike the capital market, banks as a financer are more closed to corporates as they also provide fee-based services. Banks have the opportunity to have and collect more information on corporate behaviour, including information related to sustainability. Through this constant engagement, banks can have dialogues and influence corporates to integrate sustainability in their business decision-making. Banks can also share best practices and business models related to sustainability in various industries during this engagement. It is a win-win situation for corporates and banks as sustainability is not a risk but an opportunity to grow businesses.

Why We Need Transition Bonds[1]

Globally, the industrial sector accounts for nearly 30 per cent of greenhouse gas (GHG) emissions and India is no different. And maintaining the 2°C temperature goal, as envisaged in the 2015 Paris Agreement, requires transitioning this sector. If you consider hard-to-abate industries such as shipping and aviation, chemicals, steel and cement, decarbonisation is a complex process and transformation happens in a series of phases. Such brown industries require major investments to achieve any significant reduction in emissions. To add to this, traditional forms of sustainable finance usually do not classify investments in these business activities as 'green'. And this is where transition bonds come in.

Bridging Green and Brown

Transition bond is a class of debt instruments that maintain the transparency and rigour that characterise green bonds but are designed to be more inclusive in their standards. Unlike green bonds that are earmarked to raise money for climate and environmental projects, transition bonds can be issued by firms aspiring to reduce their GHG emissions. In other words, these bonds enable entities that would otherwise not qualify to issue green bonds to obtain sustainability-related financing.

The money can be used for activities that reduce the environmental impact of the business, such as carbon capture and storage, decommissioning coal plants, waste-to-energy or exclusively financing new and/or existing eligible transition projects. Financing capital equipment costs, particularly in heavy industries, is a good use case. Often, the specialised capital equipment used have long replacement cycles and require a substantial investment for upgradation. The decommissioning also requires many steps including remediation and restoration of the project site, in addition to construction of a new facility.

The bonds specify what they hope to achieve with the investment and these precise milestones and objectives provide investors with clarity on the overlap in goals for issuer and investors. For instance, a thermal power utility issuing transition bond seeks to achieve emissions rate of 90 gCO2/kWh,

---

[1] The article was written by Labanya Prakash Jena, and Shreyans Jain and was first published by the Hindu Business Line. https://www.thehindubusinessline.com/opinion/why-we-need-transition-bonds/article65293161.ece

which would be suitable for what investors are looking for, say, projects that achieve emissions rate of 100 gCO2/kWh. The bond's time horizon also has to be aligned with the key performance indicators achieved to avoid mismatch.

One good example of an industry that can benefit from transition bonds is cement. India's cement industries contribute about 8 per cent to the country's total GHG emissions. Carbon intensity in production can be reduced by 48 per cent by investing in a combination of existing technologies such as carbon capture storage (CCS), renewable technologies and intermediate product substitutes.

Small Sliver

Transition bonds can play a significant role in mobilising capital at scale for accelerated industrial decarbonisation. S&P Global estimates transition finance, including issuance, to contribute as much as $1 trillion to the estimated $3 trillion of annual investments needed to limit global warming to 2°C by 2050.

Despite the potential, transition bonds have so far played only a small role as a financing solution to decarbonise hard-to-abate sectors. According to BloombergNEF, the transition finance market has seen $11.5 billion in the issuance of 24 transition bonds since its inception. This compares to $1.7 trillion and $391 billion for green and social bonds, respectively.

The slow growth of the transition bond market can be attributed to the non-availability of a clear definition of what transition finance actually means and to what extent such instruments are environmentally sustainable. This has fuelled scepticism among investors about this debt instrument becoming yet another tool for 'transition washing'.

That said, there is much room for optimism, as seen in the case of Cadent Gas, the largest distributor of gas in Great Britain. In March 2020, it was the first company in the UK to utilise sustainable debt finance to enable its low-carbon transition. The use of proceeds was outlined for retrofit of gas transmission and distribution networks, renewable energy, clean transportation and energy efficient buildings. The bond was oversubscribed 8.4x indicating investors' keen appetite.

Way Forward

The financial materiality of transition risks arising due to policy, regulation, legal and market changes is going to require brown industries to increase their efforts and allocate more capital for adapting to climate change. Though still in early stages, the issuance of transition bonds is following the International Capital Market Association (ICMA) guidelines on climate transition finance. These guidelines provide common expectations to capital markets participants on the practices, actions and disclosures to be made available when raising funds in debt markets for climate transition-related purposes. However, securities regulators can put statutory regulations in place for the commitments required by companies to be eligible for transition bonds.

India's E-bus Adoption has a Financing Bottleneck[1]

India launched an ambitious National Electric Bus Program (NEBP) in 2022 to deploy an additional 50,000 electric buses over five years, backed by a significant investment of $10 billion (Rs 820 billion). So far progress has been slow. Of the 359,432 buses registered between April 2015 (the inception of the Faster Adoption and Manufacturing of Electric Vehicles (FAME) scheme) and May 2023, only 4,506 are electric—that's just 1.25 per cent.

The government has adopted a two-fold approach to achieve the NEBP target. First, Union government-owned Convergence Energy Services Limited (CESL) is implementing the demand aggregation model, negotiating competitive prices for electric buses by leveraging economies of scale. Second, the gross cost contract (GCC) model involves e-bus original equipment manufacturers (OEMs) providing electric buses on a lease, with payment determined per kilometre.

There are challenges in the existing approach, particularly concerning the weak financials of State Road Transport Undertakings (SRTUs), who will operate these buses. A Union government-owned dedicated e-bus financing facility can help overcome these challenges.

Challenges for OEMs

The recent CES electric bus tender, valued at Rs 50 billion ($610 million), faced setbacks as major automotive OEMs refrained from bidding. The OEMs are sceptical of delayed payments by the SRTUs because of the latter's poor financial health and operating performance. According to the latest financial data from the Ministry of Road Transport and Highways (MoRTH), the 56 SRTUs collectively have a debt of Rs 380 billion ($4.6 billion) and had a combined net loss of approximately Rs 180 billion ($2.2 billion) in the fiscal year (FY) 2018–19.

Further, becoming bus operators under the current GCC model may not be desirable for the OEMs as it does not align with their core business. Besides, the OEMs will have to hold electric buses on their balance sheet and source

[1] The article was written by Labanya Prakash Jena and Saurabh Trivedi and was published by Institute for Energy Economics and Financial Analysis. https://ieefa.org/resources/accelerating-indias-electric-bus-adoption-fuelled-strategic-financing-facility

capital to finance them, impeding their ability to increase manufacturing capacities that may not be in the best interest of India's e-vehicle adoption plan. Therefore, while the government's implementation of a payment security mechanism (PSM) addresses delayed-payment concerns, the balance sheet risk remains unresolved. This calls for a re-evaluation of the financing approach.

Electric bus Financing Programme

An electric bus financing programme can mitigate these challenges and cut the high upfront costs for the SRTUs. This programme would be owned and run by a financial institution under Union government control. The institution for public electric bus financing will resemble the financing technique of Indian Railway Finance Corporation (IRFC) and the Indian Renewable Energy Development Agency (IREDA).

This programme would aggregate funds for e-buses for the SRTUs. It will procure the e-buses from OEMs via a tender process managed by the CESL and enter into operating lease agreements with the SRTUs for either the entire bus or just the batteries. The SRTUs will also establish separate service and maintenance contracts with the OEMs for the efficient operation and upkeep of e-buses—this will help keep the collateral value of the e-buses intact. Moreover, the programme can become a one-stop shop for financing other zero-emission vehicles, including private sector ones.

Capitalisation and Financing Sources

Capitalising this programme would be the responsibility of the nodal financial institution, which can tap into public and private sources. Public financing can come from the Union government's FAME subsidy (financial incentives for electric vehicles), development finance institutions (DFIs) and international public finance, including multilateral development banks (MDBs) and donors. Private financing could come from commercial banks, capital markets and other private financiers. This blend of public and private financing can significantly reduce the capital cost for the financing programme. Lastly, the financing programme can generate additional revenue by selling carbon credits derived from the emissions avoided by leasing electric buses.

Advantages

International climate financiers, including MDBs/DFIs, typically prefer providing capital through Union government-controlled entities rather than private companies or state governments. Such financers, mandated to invest in climate-friendly assets, can offer concessional capital and risk mitigation solutions, such as partial risk guarantees, to the facility. Moreover, private financiers may be more inclined to invest in the financing programme if public financiers take a riskier position in its capital structure.

Challenges can be Solved

Provisions for proper recycling and compliance with environmental standards are essential to prevent retired buses from re-entering the market. Such strong Climate Change commitments are crucial for attracting international climate finance.

A PSM is necessary even with the proposed e-bus financing programme. However, such a model can address the financial challenges the SRTUs face while not impacting the OEMs. The financing programme can play a crucial role in accelerating the transition to sustainable public transportation in India.

CLIMATE FINANCE: THE ROLE OF INTERNATIONAL INSTITUTIONS

How De-risking Renewable Investments can Bridge the $1.2 Trillion Gap in Developing Countries[1]

To meet ambitious global climate goals, we need to mobilise $1.7 trillion annually in investments in renewable energy. The adoption of renewable energy (RE) technology in developing countries is significantly less than desired. We need to invest $1.7 trillion every year in developing countries—in 2022, we hit $544 billion. To close that $1.2 trillion gap, de-risking private capital is key. This deficit is one of the key constraints stifling the adoption of the RE sector in developing countries. There are several risks preventing capital flows to the RE sector in developing countries. Among them, credit risk is key.

In the last two decades, international institutions and financial intermediaries innovated and deployed credit risk-mitigation instruments. However, these instruments are not currently being used to their maximum potential. The high cost of these instruments, cumbersome process, inflexibility, lack of awareness and slow decision-making by multilateral institutions and governments is limiting the use of existing credit risk-mitigating instruments—and slowing the energy transition.

The Asian Development Bank's Partial Credit Guarantee

In the early days of solar energy in India, the Asian Development Bank (ADB) provided a partial credit guarantee (PCG) for addressing credit risk in utility-scale solar lending in India. The idea was to provide broader comfort to lenders in a new space. However, the PCG programme has not been successful yet; only two RE issuers have used this instrument to raise funds. Delayed deployment of the facility, changed perceptions in the interim, high perceived cost of availing the guarantee, cumbersome process to understand the mechanism, inflexibility and limited awareness have prevented wider uptake. Addressing these barriers, primarily increasing the flexibility of offers, reducing the complexity of transactions and subsidising guarantee

---

[1] The article was written by Labanya Prakash Jena and Gireesh Shrimali and was first published by the World Economic Forum. https://www.weforum.org/agenda/2024/02/financial-instruments-key-to-hitting-1-trillion-in-green-investments/

fees, can greatly increase its adoption, which can attract massive amounts of private capital.

The International Finance Corporation's Partial Credit Guarantee

The PCG guarantees offered by the International Finance Corporation (IFC) are growing over time, primarily supporting local currency financing. These guarantees have improved tenors but their impact on cost of capital is less clear. Likewise, risk-sharing facilities (RSFs), another instrument of IFC aiming to address credit risk, have shown mixed results.

Guarantee instruments are fringe activity to the IFC's primary activity: direct investment. They are one-offs given the IFC's focus on project finance, plus the incentives for the provision of these guarantees are misaligned, given IFC's focus on large deals. In addition, the IFC's risk-averse approach also handcuffs its use of guarantee instruments.

To increase the use of these guarantees, the IFC needs to institutionalise innovation in offering and reduce complexity in transactions. It should focus on guarantee (instead of treating it as a fringe activity), increase the size of guarantee funds and add more human capacity to scale up the instruments that crowd in large-scale private sector investment.

The Credit Guarantee Mechanism

The credit guarantee mechanism (CGM) was developed to address credit risks in lending to the rooftop solar sector in India in the medium and small size enterprise (MSME) segment, in the context of India's ambitious target of 40 GW of rooftop solar capacity by 2022. The instrument has a leverage of approximately nine—meaning \$1 of commitment to the CGM catalyses \$9 in private sector lending.

Given the World Bank's interest in supporting the rooftop sector in India and its ongoing support to the State Bank of India (SBI), the implementation of CGM was passed over to these institutions in 2018. Quick decision-making in international institutions and prioritising the MSME in India's green transition can make this catalytic financial instrument run. The same instrument can also be deployed in other developing countries, where the credit risks in the MSME segment is the same in most of the countries.

Off-grid Solutions to De-risk Green Investments

First-loss guarantee (FLG), an instrument in which a third party compensates the lender if the borrower defaults, is another catalytic instrument in the initial stages of a sector like renewables, given the general discomfort of financiers, evolving to PCGs as the sector matures. These guarantees have been provided for various businesses by various agencies over time. Take, for example, the US International Development Finance Corporation (DFC)'s \$10 million guarantee to catalyse \$20 million in loans by Trine or MIGA's \$5.9 million guarantee to the \$100 million fund by BBox.

Another novel solution in the off-grid solar financing space is the Green 4 Access platform in Africa. Three years after conceptualisation, Green 4 Access is still in fundraise mode. In this context, a key resource in Africa is the Africa Guarantee Fund (AGF), focused on mobilising private resources for SME resources in Africa, which has enabled \$1.6 billion in financing for SMEs in Africa. Using learnings from the AGF, solutions such as Green 4 Access can be further scaled and replicated elsewhere. To this end, learnings from Bangladesh's successful solar home system (SHS) programme, facilitated by the Infrastructure Development Company Limited (IDCOL), could be instructive.

IDCOL was set up as an intermediary financial institution to provide grants and low interest loans to partner organisations. IDCOL was able to do so due to grants and credit support provided by various multilateral institutions. In this process, IDCOL was able to address the credit risk of the eventual customers.

However, the MSME segment faces similar issues to traditional guarantee providers: small size, lack of flexibility of guarantee to meet sector specific needs and slow decision-making processes of the institutions providing guarantees.

To scale up these instruments, multilateral development banks, bilateral financial institutions and donor agencies must make credit guarantee a core product offering and increase awareness of its product offerings. The guarantor's balance sheet must be replenished through grants and concessional capital to scale up the use of these instruments. Credit guarantors must be flexible to accommodate the varying needs of developing nations and agile to meet the urgent needs of these countries.

Impeding Climate Finance: International Finance Corporation Seems to have a Rather Risk-averse Capital Deployment Strategy[1]

The G20 meeting in September is the final chance for one of the most crucial items on the agenda—Multilateral Development Bank (MDB) reform. The International Finance Corporation (IFC), a member of the World Bank Group, plays a crucial role in promoting private sector investment in developing countries. However, a critical analysis of IFC's capital deployment strategy reveals a risk-averse approach that may hinder its ability to drive capital for sustainable development.

The IFC's substantial cash holdings raise questions about its effectiveness as a development finance institution. It is missing opportunities to provide much-needed capital for sustainable projects. Since IFC is not a deposit-taking institution, its cash reserves far exceed what is necessary for operational and financing purposes. By the end of 2022, IFC held \$32.5 billion of capital available to absorb potential losses against a total asset base of \$99 billion, while capital required to maintain an AAA credit rating is \$20.1 billion, as per IFC's statement. Reducing the cash buffer will release \$12.4 billion of liquidity to deploy into high-impact projects.

Although IFC operates in developing countries, 1.6 times the conservative debt-to-equity is still not justified. Indian Non-Banking financial company's debt-to-equity ratio is approximately six times. By exercising a more aggressive approach to debt financing, the IFC could effectively leverage its balance sheet and maximise its impact by channelling additional funds into sustainable development projects.

Over the past five years, IFC has typically mobilised about 80 cents of external capital for every dollar it invested, as it always protects itself from downside risk. Given the multi-trillion-dollar climate and development challenges and IFC's limited assets of ~\$100 billion, this mobilisation rate needs to increase. Embracing more innovative instruments, such as first-loss guarantees and partial credit guarantees, can crowd in additional private

[1] The article was written by Labanya Prakash Jena and Alexander H. Rutter and was first published by the Financial Express. https://www.financialexpress.com/opinion/impeding-climate-finance-international-finance-corporation-seems-to-have-a-rather-risk-averse-capital-deployment-strategy/3210610/

capital. IFC can invest in the 'first' 20 per cent of projects, crowding in private capital for the remainder. IFC should target private capital mobilisation on the order of 5:1 rather than 0.8:1.

Currently, IFC does not take on technology or commercial risks and tends to invest in companies that already have an established credit history and can access private financing. It should assume these risks that private financiers are not yet comfortable which warrants credit underwriting practices be less conservative, thereby attracting a higher proportion of private capital in projects.

In 2022, IFC's exposure to the financial market and fund was 48 per cent. By relying on financial markets and funds to determine project selection, the IFC exposes itself to the risk of ESG-washing, where projects with limited environmental or social impact receive funding.

As a global institution, IFC invests and borrows in diverse currencies, with USD borrowings accounting for just 42 per cent of borrowing. IFC's largest exposure is 10.5 per cent of its portfolio (India) and its top three investees (India, Brazil and China) are all relatively stable countries with minimal currency risk. Private sector investors regularly take unhedged risks in these markets, building in currency exchange rate risk as part of their expected risk vs. return profile. In contrast, IFC hedges on every transaction and passes this cost onto borrowers, making capital more expensive and, therefore, less impactful than even commercial financial institutions. The conservative currency hedging policy locks clients into higher rates with IFC than is available in the market.

The IFC's increasing average lending and investment size suggests a bias towards large projects as well. An analysis of 450 recent projects suggested an average investment size of $88 million. Just 8.5 per cent of projects were for an investment of less than $10 million. This bias towards larger projects may limit the IFC's ability to support smaller-scale initiatives that can have a profound effect on inclusive growth. It means that investments tend to go to large, well-banked firms that do not necessarily need IFC's support. Diversifying investment sizes and embracing a more inclusive approach would allow the IFC to reach a broader range of projects and play a more catalytic role in investing in startups and companies promoting innovative solutions in emerging fields like battery storage, green hydrogen, EVs, etc.

The excessive compliance requirements for IFC investments, regardless of project size, is another challenge for small companies. The excessive compliance costs deter small projects and work in favour of large companies with extensive armies of accountants and lawyers.

While IFC is vital in stimulating private sector investment in developing countries, its capital deployment strategy exhibits a risk-averse approach that hampers its potential for driving sustainable development. As a development institution, IFC should be at the forefront of being more aggressive in taking risks that the private sector will not and crowding in further private sector investment. Instead, it has shown a more conservative approach than private investors, limiting its additionality and development impact.

Debt Restructuring of Vulnerable Countries[1]

Need for Immediate Debt Restructuring

Several developing and vulnerable countries, particularly small island developing states (SIDS), are facing severe challenges from multiple fronts, including unsustainable public debt, low foreign currency reserves, soaring inflation, a shortage of necessities and a dwindling economy. On one side, they need to invest heavily in climate action to protect themselves from devastating climate-related extreme weather events such as hurricanes, storms, droughts, heat waves, floods and sea-level rise. On the other side, many of them have ambitious plans to transition towards a green economy. Unfortunately, they do not have the fiscal muscles to mobilise the necessary capital for their climate actions. Amidst this situation, debt restructuring through climate change lenses will offer much-needed relief to these countries to make themselves climate-resilient and support global actions to mitigate climate risk.

While it is imperative to rejuvenate the economy, without a thought of the environment, it could lead to environmental disaster and, consequently, possible macroeconomic instability. Unfortunately, most of the existing sovereign debt restructuring programmes do not incorporate climate-change risk and biodiversity loss even if they are potential risks to macroeconomic and financial stability. A climate-resilient economy will support the country's macroeconomic stability efforts. The primary goal of the debt restructuring programme is to offer liquidity to achieve macroeconomic stability and quick recovery of the economy. However, there are specific ways a debt restructuring programme can offer long-term environmental benefits without hampering the debt restructuring programme's primary goals. The twin goals can be complementary instead of competing, even though the primary goal is focused on the short and medium-term gains, while the benefits of climate action will be realised in the long term.

Debt for Nature Swaps or Debt for Sustainability will Offer Dual Benefits

A sovereign debt restructuring programme layout a debt relief programme from the creditors. Debt relief could be debt reductions, maturity extensions, grace periods, provision of concessional financing, debt swaps and changes in interest rates. 'Debt swap' is one of the debt restructuring programmes

[1] The article was written by Labanya Prakash Jena and was first published by the Observer Research Foundation. https://www.orfonline.org/expert-speak/debt-restructuring-of-vulnerable-countries

where new bonds will replace the existing bonds with revised clauses. Debt swap offers multiple benefits to a country reeling under a debt crisis: infusing much-needed liquidity; reducing a debt overhang and the country's external vulnerability; buying back existing debt at a discount and preventing financial crisis. Reducing or extension of debt stock or debt services payment stabilises the economy and stimulates economic growth and investment. 'DFC swaps' or 'debt for sustainability' is one of the debt-for-swap tools to restructure sovereign debt. DFC swap involves an agreement between the sovereign state and creditors to reduce some of the borrowing country's debt in exchange for commitments, to invest in climate and natural outcomes.

DFC swap offers traditional debt swap benefits. It will also help vulnerable countries build a climate-resilient economy by accessing international financial and technical assistance. Debt for nature swaps is not new; this kind of transaction was earlier implemented in many countries, including Bolivia, Ecuador, Indonesia and Seychelles. However, the transaction size was small. Conservation International bought back Bolivian bank debt face value of US$650,000 at an 85 per cent discount in exchange for legal protection of rainforest land and covering the operating costs for a reserve of 2.7 million acres. In the DFC structure, there are enough incentives for the governments of these countries to get the necessary financial support for quick economic recovery and much-needed restoration of the country's environment.

The Mechanism, Steps and Partners

There are various ways the transactions can be implemented. One of them is the sovereign state can swap existing foreign debt with local currency debt—the proceeds are used in climate-friendly projects. Another way is existing debt is replaced with new debt with better terms and conditions and provides additional debt for climate actions. This debt restructuring will give countries some breathing space on external debt payment and fiscal capacity to invest in climate actions. There will be a condition attached to this transaction—additional debts can be forgiven if proceeds of debt are used for climate-friendly projects and achieve the desired and pre-determined results. The climate-friendly projects can be climate-resilient low-emission agriculture, soil and water conservation and management, sustainable green cover and biodiversity and the adoption of green energy. A structure can be created that incentivises the government to invest in climate-related projects. In both cases, key performance indicators (KPIs) are pre-determined.

On one side of the structure, some creditors have given to these countries, and on the other side, there are multilateral agencies, bilateral institutions (other states), donors, Development Financial Institutions (DFIs) and Environmental, Social and Corporate governance (ESG) investors who want to exchange debt for climate actions. While DFIs and multilateral agencies have a developmental agenda to enter into this transaction, bilateral institutions in this transaction are to improve the bilateral relationships with countries strategically important to them. The governments, particularly in the neighbouring countries, have strategic and economic incentives to support these countries as economic instability in the country could destabilise the peace in the region again. The ESG investors could be interested in this transaction if a structure is designed with the help of public financers (multilateral agencies, governments, etc.) so they can generate financial returns. DFC swaps can promote climate action and potentially contribute to macroeconomic stability. They possess the potential to be an exceptional tool within the realm of international public finance, as they enable the achievement of long-term environmental advantages while simultaneously fulfilling developmental goals.

Boosting Climate Finance[1]

That there are significant shortfalls in meeting climate finance commitments by developed countries is no breaking news. But given the urgency of the need vis-à-vis the delays on the other, there is a need to explore creative but tested solutions to bridge the gap. One category that may hold promise is credit enhancement instruments such as guarantees, subordinated debt, grants and equities.

The key sources of international climate finance are multilateral development banks (MDBs) such as World Bank and Asian Development Bank; international development financial institutions such as International Finance Corporation (IFC) and UN-backed international climate funds (Green Climate Fund, Climate Investment Fund) and bilateral funding. Typically, climate financiers use four categories of instruments to fund green projects—equity, loan, risk management instruments and grants/ technical assistance. The last category is a small amount and all others are direct financial support for large infrastructure and other development projects.

There is a need for large capital by poor countries to combat climate change—estimated by economists Nicholas Stern and Vera Songwe at over $2 trillion per year by 2030. By comparison, the total disbursement of capital by World Bank Group in 2022 was only $88 billion. There is hence a clear need to unlock private capital, given the staggering need.

However, there are a few issues that discourage private investments. First is the need for risk reduction through long-term and patient capital without which many projects become too risky for private investors to consider. Second, given the capital-intensive nature of clean-tech investments and the higher cost of capital in poor countries, there is a need for subsidising the cost of finance to make projects viable. This however makes the returns not commensurate with the project risks, for a private investor. A study by Kenny, Kalow and Ramachandran suggests that IFC's portfolio has become less risky over time, which is slowing down capital flows to sectors that need public financial support.

---

[1] The article was written by Labanya Prakash Jena, and Meera Siva and was first published by the *Hindu Business Line*. https://www.thehindubusinessline.com/opinion/boosting-climate-finance/article66619821.ece

Credit Enhancements

Rather than provide loans and, lately equity, use of credit enhancement instruments such as guarantees or subordinate debt, can help crowd-in private capital. Let us illustrate the leverage one can get from simple default guarantees. Consider a debt portfolio of $1 billion with an expected default rate of 10 per cent. A partial guarantee of 50 per cent by MDB needs a credit guarantee fund of $50 million. So, we can get a leverage of 20x to unlock $1 billion by setting up a credit guarantee of $50 million.

Despite the large power of leverage, guarantees represent only a small portion of the total investment portfolio of MDBs. Since MDBs treat guarantees on the same basis as a loan in their book, there is no financial benefit for using guarantees instead of a loan from the shareholder perspective. Remarkably, the IBRD was envisaged as a guarantee institution, not a lending institution.

Similarly, a subordinate bond, junior than senior bond in the capital structure, can attract private financiers as well. For example, a subordinate debt from MDBs that contributes 30 per cent of debt in the capital structure can give enough comfort to private senior debt-holders to invest in the project as the latter have the first rights over the assets. The public capital leverage will be 2x.

However, data shows that DFIs currently take the less risky senior debt positions in the capital structure of the project. A study by ODI on blended finance suggests that senior debt accounts for 72 per cent of blended concessional investment by MDBs and DFIs. If MDBs continue to be conservative in lending and equity investment and have an investment strategy that is similar to a private investment, it will miss out on its important role—attracting private capital.

Climate Funds: Developed Nations Must Step Up[1]

In 2009, at the COP15 Summit in Copenhagen, developed countries committed to jointly mobilise $100 billion a year for climate finance so that developing nations can take effective actions. The 2015 Paris Summit extended this goal through 2025. The world saw several hydro-meteorological (floods, storms, heat waves) and climatological (droughts, wildfires) disasters, largely attributed to climate change, during this period. Unsurprisingly, the less endowed and vulnerable countries suffered disproportionately. But the promised funding remained elusive. Not just that, instead of covering the shortfall, developed countries are now coercing developing nations into committing to an unreasonable target of reducing carbon emissions to net-zero by mid-century. What will fix the widening chasm?

Inconsistent Estimation

There are many disconnects, not just in the needs, but also in basics such as estimations on funds disbursed, as a proper methodology is not used in estimating the actual finance mobilised by developed countries towards the $100-billion obligation. For example, based on recent estimates of the Organisation for Economic Co-operation and Development (OECD), climate finance provided and mobilised by developed countries amounted to $79.6 billion in 2019. These estimates are, however, disputed unequivocally by most recipient countries. The Climate Finance Shadow Report 2020, published by Oxfam, for instance, estimates climate finance flows at $22.5 billion in 2017–18—only about a third of the $71 billion estimated by the OECD for the same period.

Such inconsistency in estimating international climate finance arises primarily because of two key issues related to the taxonomy of international climate finance: Clubbing development finance with climate finance and counting private finance as financial support.

Private non-grant capital, by virtue of its commercial orientation cannot be termed international climate finance. Nor can development assistance provided by multilateral banks and development finance institutions for

[1] The article was written by Labanya Prakash Jena, and Shreyans Jain and was first published by the *Hindu Business Line*. https://www.thehindubusinessline.com/opinion/climate-funds-developed-nations-must-step-up/article38135366.ece

infrastructure projects be classified as climate finance. These resources, used for the construction of roads or setting up electricity transmission and distribution infrastructure, for example, can be mobilised by developing countries in a business-as-usual scenario without any assistance from developed countries. To reduce the risk of 'greenwashing' and cover the risks and costs of climate externalities, climate finance must be new and incremental. Furthermore, only the grant-equivalent element of any claimed disbursement should be counted as climate finance.

Another cause of concern is the significantly low amount allocated for climate adaptation. Article 9.4 of the Paris Agreement states that the provision of scaled-up financial resources should aim to balance adaptation and mitigation. In 2016, the United Nations Environment Programme (UNEP), in its Adaptation Gap Report, estimated the annual climate adaptation costs and financing needs at $140–300 billion by 2030 and $280–500 billion by 2050. In 2019, the OECD estimated the share of climate adaptation finance at $20.1 billion of the total $79.6 billion tracked.

One plausible reason for the higher investment in mitigation projects is that they are politically popular as they lead to a reduction in carbon emission—a global public good that benefits everyone, including the donor country. Such investments also bring international recognition for being 'climate conscious' as project outcomes are clearly visible and measurable. Climate mitigation projects are investable, which attract private financiers. On the contrary, adaptation sectors find it difficult to attract funds, especially private capital, due to high project development costs and lack of commercial viability or good investment returns. The benefits are also largely confined to the recipient countries.

Action Plan

To make up for the shortfall and fulfilment of internationally agreed climate objectives by 2030, the developed countries must take immediate action. First, there is a need for clarity and consensus on the definition of international climate finance to put all controversies surrounding the classification of 'climate relevant' projects to rest. This includes creating a taxonomy to make a clear distinction between development finance and climate finance and avoid possibilities of 'greenwashing'.

Second, climate adaptation finance must be ramped up. Denmark, for instance, has committed to allocating 60 per cent of its climate finance to adaptation projects.

Third, international climate finance should be allocated to recipient countries on a need basis. Despite having a relatively smaller share in global greenhouse gas emissions historically, climate change vulnerable nations such Pacific Island Countries (PICs), Small Island Developing Countries (SIDs) and Least Developed Countries (LDCs) are disproportionally affected by climate change.

Fourth, the $100-billion target should be revised to reflect the true extent of finance required to respond to existing and future adverse consequences of climate change. The post-2025 outlook should reflect a significant upward trend in the uptake of international climate finance by developed countries.

US$ 1 Trillion for Renewable Energy: Transforming Multilateral Agencies[1]

Developing countries need US$ 1 trillion of green capital per annum in the renewable energy (RE) sector alone by 2030 to meet their net-zero targets, according to the International Monetary Fund (IMF). However, the total capital mobilised in the RE sector was less than US$ 495 billion in 2022; most of this mobilisation was restricted to the developed countries. This is not in line with the commitments made in the Paris Conference of Parties (COP) 21. Developing countries struggle to raise the required amount of capital efficiently and quickly due to the smaller size of their economies, limited financial savings, limited fiscal power and the need for significant investment in other strategic areas. Moreover, several developing countries are already under a severe debt burden that has crippled their abilities to raise more public capital for climate actions, including investment in the revenue-generating RE sector. Without a large-scale intervention by multilateral and bilateral institutions, it is nearly impossible for developing countries to mobilise the required amount of capital to meet their clean energy needs. On the other side, several developing countries rely heavily on fossil fuels for their energy generation ramp-up plans to cater to their economic growth agendas. Hence, the active participation of developing countries in the clean energy transition is crucial. This will strengthen global efforts to decarbonise the energy sector and consequently help achieve its net-zero targets.

Banking Finance: Not the Most Efficient for the RE Sector

The RE sector needs long-term debt funding. As the cost of debt funding is lower than equity in most cases, it brings down the cost of funding, thereby, making RE tariff competitive. Banks are not modelled for long-term financing as their liability duration acceptance is relatively short. Typically, banks would prefer financing selective RE projects for the medium term. They tend to renew such loans for additional terms unless the asset quality significantly deteriorates. However, the revised terms of credit depend on the credit quality of assets and the prevailing interest rates. Such a change in

[1] The article was written by Labanya Prakash Jena and Prasad Ashok Thakur and was first published by the Observer Research Foundation. https://www.orfonline.org/expert-speak/us-1-trillion-for-renewable-energy

terms of credit, including an increase in interest rate, may expose borrowers (RE project developers) to refinancing risk. Thus, developers typically wish to avoid using medium-duration loans and prefer to lock in interest rates for the longest time possible.

In reality, banks in developing countries are already heavily exposed to long-term infrastructure assets. Hence, they have exhausted their resources in meeting the long-term funding needs of the RE sector. Besides, banks have to charge a higher interest rate on long-term loans as risk weightage is higher for long-term assets, due to the BASEL framework, compared to short-term assets. Thus, the capital market remains the only option on the table to solve the long-term debt funding requirement of the RE sector.

Preference of the Capital Market

Capital markets can offer efficient long-term debt financing solutions at a reasonable rate to the RE sector. The primary financers in the capital market can be large institutional investors such as pension and insurance companies, presently holding more than US$100 trillion of assets under management. These two sets of investors need long-duration and low-risk assets with predictable cash flows to meet long-duration predictable liabilities. They prefer to invest in liquid securities and low-risk traded fixed-income securities to meet their long-duration liabilities. Here, the RE sector can offer a solution; this sector is typically capital-intensive at the construction and development stage, followed by very low annual fixed and variable costs along with a contractual revenue structure. This allows it to offer reasonably steady, low-risk and long-term cash flows. This allows for a match between institutional investors' investment characteristics. Thus, presently, more than half of the proceeds of green bonds targeting institutional investors are used to finance the RE sector.

Solving the Credit Rating Challenge in Developing Countries

The credit rating of RE bonds can turn out to be low in the financial markets. Thus, low risk-seeking large institutional investors in developed countries, such as pension funds and insurance companies, may be averse to buying these debt securities issued by RE developers in developing countries. Here, Multilateral Development Banks (MDBs), Development Finance Institutions (DFIs) and similar public financial institutions can play an important role. They can offer partial credit guarantees (PCG) so that the credit rating of these bonds can be upgraded. Such guarantees by AAA-rated global public financial institutions such as the World Bank and Asian Development Bank can make the loan asset less risky, resulting in its credit rating improvement. The quantum of the guarantee can be changed over the years. As the risk may materialise in the long term, guarantee coverage may increase with the passage of time to mitigate long-term risk. Credit guarantee by public financial institutions sends a positive signal to private investors about the bankability of the project. The investors will also be ensured that corporate governance issues are held at bay and political risk is controlled.

The Multiplier Effect of a Guarantee is Bigger than the Loan and Technical Assistance

The amount of capital that the public financial institutions currently have will not be enough to meet the funding needs of the entire RE sector globally. One of the ways to increase capital flows is by leveraging its balance sheet by offering PCG. As a result, a multiplying effect is triggered as compared to a vanilla loan and/or equity. Now, the mobilisation of large-scale private capital is possible by optimally deploying public capital. MDBs and DFIs need to disburse capital only when a guarantee is triggered—in case there is a default of bonds. This means that DFIs and MDBs do not have to deploy a large amount of capital upfront. It will only be summoned when a guarantee is triggered. As several RE projects in developing countries have political and regulatory risks, MDBs and DFIs also have the advantage of preventing developing countries from defaulting on their bonds or taking any decision that leads to the default of loans.

Exponentially Increasing the Impact of Guarantees

It is proposed that the deployment of financial guarantees can be further optimised beyond a partial credit guarantee. When it comes to renewable energy, it is a well-understood fact that such investments yield returns in the form of active cash flows during the life of the project. Also, increasingly, the liquidity of such investments/assets is high as there are several project developers in the market interested in taking over stressed/defunct assets. Thus, in projects where the climate action interventions yield cash flows and/or have intrinsic value, it is wise for the MDB/DFIs to provide a partial credit guarantee only for the interest component of the debt. Such an approach will help pool in more private sector investments while freeing up MDB/DFI capital for a larger number of diverse climate action projects globally. This is also in line with the function of the MDB/DFIs to act as a magnet to attract multiple stakeholders and stimulate interaction between them.

Since MDBs and DFIs have a higher appetite to take risks in comparison to private capital, they should focus on de-risking projects to attract private capital for climate action. To remain relevant, MDB and DFIs should re-calibrate their capital deployment strategy. By serving as a bridge between adaptation/mitigation projects and private investors, risk-mitigating instruments like partial credit guarantees can contribute towards delivering climate justice to developing countries.

How to Close the World's $1 Trillion Renewable Energy Gap[1]

If net-zero is to be achieved by 2050, the investment gap per year in the renewable energy sector in emerging and developing economies (EMDE) is $1.35 trillion. This massive gap is across the renewable energy sector, including solar, which is critical for decarbonising energy systems. Access to capital continues to be a challenge for solar in EMDE. Like the infrastructure sector, solar is capital intensive and has a long gestation period and generates spillover benefits which for various types of investors is not suitable. In addition, banks—key financiers in the EMDE—are structurally unwieldy for financing solar projects: They limit their long-term loans as their liability duration impedes them from lending to the sector for the long term. There is also a refinancing risk for the borrower if financed by banks, as the solar sector needs long-term debt financing.

In EMDE, solar projects continue to be largely been financed by banks, but to effectively accelerate capital flows to this renewable energy sector, pension funds and insurance companies are more suitable as their long-term investment duration matches their long-term liabilities. The high cash-flow stability of solar, thanks to high predictability in sales volume and pricing and low and stable cash expenses over the lifetime of the project, make the sector attractive for low-risk-seeking investors.

Challenges on the Road to Solar

However, there are challenges for these institutional investors in the solar sector in EMDE. The three key ones are lack of suitable financial instruments, high risk (real and perceived) and disconnect between investors, policymakers and solar projects. Institutional investors rarely invest in solar due to the limited availability of traded financial instruments. Owing to their preference for liquid financial assets, they prefer to invest in equity, bond, structured finance, yieldco, etc. Since credit ratings of most of the bonds issued by corporates in the solar sector in EMDE are low in the domestic and

[1] The article was written by Labanya Prakash Jena and Jagjeet Sareen and was first published by the World Economic Forum. https://www.weforum.org/agenda/2022/09/renewable-energy-gap-solar-finance/

international markets, pension funds and insurance companies do not buy these bonds. They invest in low-risk fixed-income securities.

In addition, institutional investors do not have the manpower to assess risk and return propositions of direct investment, so they invest through an intermediary that can assess opportunities and invest on their behalf, like debt funds. Unfortunately, a limited number of specialised financial intermediaries in the EMDE can provide such services.

Stability through International Public Finance

Policy and regulatory uncertainties in the solar sector, lack of contractual enforcement and foreign exchange fluctuations increase the risk and expected return of financers and consequently make such projects commercially unviable. This warrants the use of risk-mitigating instruments and solutions, which can reduce risks for institutional investors. These instruments could be guarantees, insurance and other credit-enhancement instruments.

The international development and green financial institutions can provide partial credit guarantees that can help the bonds become less risky, thereby improving their credit rating. A guarantee is a better use of scarce public capital as it can attract more private capital than equity and lending.

The other way is setting up a solar debt fund that attracts these institutional investors. A blended finance structure of the fund could be instituted, where public finance is used to provide first-loss protection to private institutional investors in case of default. The first loss of protection can improve the credit profile of the fund, thereby attracting low-risk- and low-return-seeking institutional investors.

International Solar Alliance (ISA) is designing new instruments to mitigate these problems and creating channels for better access to capital from these investors. A blended finance risk mitigation facility has been developed by ISA for the solar sector in the African region that pools capital from both public and private financers. This risk mitigation facility can be replicated and scaled in other areas as well.

Coordination to Solve the Renewable Energy Gap

The investment gap has not been bridged because of a disconnect between investors, policymakers and projects. Large investors in developed countries find it challenging to invest in solar projects in EMDE as they may not have accessible networks, connections or the time to engage in structuring. This renewable energy disconnect can also be solved through intermediaries who connect capital providers and solar projects. The intermediary can facilitate a greater flow of capital towards the solar sector by sourcing deals, performing preliminary due diligence, structuring and monitoring deals and providing fiduciary management services to institutional investors.

Besides, there is a need for dialogue, knowledge-sharing and exchange of ideas for effective solar policies and to send the correct signals for investments. Multilateral organisations can set up a platform for dialogues between investors and policymakers aimed at enabling the exchange of insights, designing policy solutions on shared priorities and connecting investors, solar developers and policymakers. The aim is to build strategic partnerships between investors, policymakers and corporates to accelerate capital flows, particularly in EMDE.

Massive efforts across the system are required to fill the huge renewable energy investment gap needed to overcome the solar financing challenge. An integrated approach to resolving issues and systemic challenges that hinder solar adoption is necessary to accelerate capital flows to the sector.

Innovative instruments and strategies, resolve to achieve the common goal of increasing the use and quality of solar energy and recognising its capability to meet energy needs in a safe, convenient, affordable, equitable and sustainable manner will help achieve the intended targets as set under the Paris Agreement on our path towards achieving net-zero.

Seven Priorities for a Transformative Future

In the last ten years, India has improved tremendously in making impactful interventions towards decarbonizing its economy. As a result, carbon intensity has reduced by ~32% in the year 2022 as compared to 2005. This leap is largely attributed to the rapid adoption of renewable energy and energy efficiency technologies. As India progresses, it will continue to accelerate the adoption of renewable energy in its energy mix, electrify its transportation system, invest in energy efficiency, and decarbonize its growing industrial sector. Solar and wind are largely at commercial parity, and electric vehicles and the deployment of mass batteries for electricity storage will soon become commercial. The real challenge for India (and the world) is to completely decarbonize the industrial sectors and the electricity systems, ideally before we reach 2050. To achieve this, It needs to innovate, evolve, and adopt a vast range of technologies across energy-generation and consuming sectors, transportation, industrial processes, agriculture, and other activities that emit GHG. The transformative measures warrant specific actions from all stakeholders, including government, international institutions, regulators, banks and financial institutions, and the private sector. The actions include structural and fundamental changes in the economic system on the allocation of resources.

This concluding chapter presents a framework for the seven essential priorities driving this transformation. Together, these elements form a roadmap for a sustainable, equitable, and prosperous future.

1. Private Sector Leadership in the Net-Zero Transition

The private sector is at the forefront of the battle against climate change. As the primary engine of economic growth, innovation, and employment, businesses have a critical role in leading the net-zero transition. The responsibility of reducing greenhouse gas emissions and adopting sustainable practices cannot rest solely on governments, regulators, or international institutions; the private sector must share it.

Companies are under increasing stakeholder pressure to participate in the great transformation toward achieving net-zero emissions. This transformational force is expected to grow as the world moves to a net-zero economy. It is not just a compliance issue but a strategic opportunity for businesses. Companies that view creating a net-zero transition plan as merely another ESG checklist item risk failing to align it with their core purpose, strategy, and vision with attributes that allow them to increase their enterprise value in a net-zero economy.

The transition to a net-zero emissions business model requires more than reducing greenhouse gas (GHG) emissions; it demands a fundamental redesign of business models and capital allocation strategies. This shift is critical to the fiduciary duties of corporate directors and should be addressed at the boardroom level. Companies proactively embracing this transformation can enhance their brand reputation, increase investor confidence, boost regulatory resilience, and achieve cost reductions. By investing in low-carbon technologies, innovating new business models, and advocating for supportive policies, the private sector can catalyse systemic change, contributing to climate mitigation while unlocking new growth opportunities and value creation.

2. Government Support through Financial and Non-Financial Incentives

The role of governments in accelerating the adoption of low-carbon technologies is indispensable. Governments can shape markets, influence behaviour, and direct resources toward areas of strategic importance. To drive the net-zero transition, governments must provide financial and non-financial incentives that lower the barriers to adopting net-zero technologies and practices. Financial incentives, such as subsidies, grants, tax breaks, and low-interest loans, can significantly reduce the cost of deploying low-carbon technologies, making them more accessible to businesses and consumers. These incentives can also stimulate research and development, driving innovation in emerging net-zero technologies that can potentially transform entire industries. Below are some of the financial incentives the Government can deploy to accelerate the adoption of low-carbon technologies.

Policy	*Instruments*
Carbon pricing	Carbon taxes, Emissions trading systems (ETS), emission or energy efficiency standards, etc.
Financial support	Grants, subsidies, concessional loans, guarantees, credit enhancement, blended financing, etc.
Supporting ecosystem	Green finance taxonomy, capacity building, a platform for redressal grievances, coordination between stakeholders, and demand creation of low-carbon technologies

Grants and subsidies play a vital role in fostering the development and deployment of new technologies, acting as essential catalysts for innovation. While grants will be essential for net-zero technologies far from commercialization, subsidies will be crucial to make these technologies commercially viable.

The Government can provide low-cost capital through various mechanisms to green sectors, given that they generate positive externalities. Creating a credit guarantee mechanism can be an efficient tool to leverage public financing, which gives enough comfort to mainstream lenders/ investors to drive green lending/investing. Blended financing is another promising financial instrument for crowding in private capital.

A promising solution is building a specialized green financial institution focusing exclusively on green lending and investment. Besides loans and investment, this institution can conduct due diligence on green projects on behalf of other financers who do not have the capacity and skills to scout for and assess such projects. The institution can also source and structure deals and provide due diligence services to investors seeking direct investment in green sectors. This institution can finance early-stage green companies/ projects. It can identify and pool debt and equity financing deals and connect with appropriate investors.

In addition to financial incentives, governments must provide non-financial support through policies, regulations, and public awareness campaigns. For instance, setting ambitious climate targets and establishing clear regulatory frameworks can create a sense of urgency and direction for businesses and investors. The government plays a pivotal role in establishing a green finance taxonomy, building capacity for developing and deploying new technologies and ensuring coordination among stakeholders. Additionally, the government is responsible for driving demand creation for low-carbon technologies to accelerate the transition to a sustainable economy. The Government of India has announced its plan to implement a Carbon Credit Trading Scheme by 2026. The government must ensure that the carbon pricing mechanism effectively drives significant reductions in greenhouse gas emissions and fosters a transition to a low-carbon economy.

Government support is crucial in creating the conditions necessary for the net-zero transition. By providing a stable and predictable policy environment, governments can encourage long-term investment in sustainable infrastructure and technologies, paving the way for a low-carbon future.

3. Innovation in Business Models and Financial Mechanisms

The transition to a net-zero economy requires technological innovation and the development of new business models and financial mechanisms that can drive capital toward sustainable solutions. Traditional business models, which often prioritize short-term profits over long-term sustainability, must be reimagined to align with the goals of the net-zero transition.

Innovative business models prioritizing low-carbon technologies, circularity, and resource efficiency are essential for reducing the environmental impact of economic activities. Business models that leverage digital technologies, such as the sharing economy and platform-based solutions, can optimize resource use and reduce the carbon footprint of various sectors.

In parallel, there is a need for innovative financial mechanisms that can mobilize the vast amounts of capital required for the net-zero transition. All these net-zero technologies are capital-intensive and have a high gestation period. Numerous challenges are associated with these technologies: lack of investment instruments, unfavourable risk/return matrix, unfavourable regulation, and high perceived risk. So, there is a need to innovate risk-mitigating instruments and solutions to reduce risks for investors. These instruments can mitigate risks associated with the sector and attract low-cost and long-term investors. These instruments could be guarantees, insurance, and other credit enhancement instruments. These innovative financial instruments can improve the risk-reward ratio of private financers, reduce the cost of capital over the project's lifetime, mobilize additional private capital compared to the business-as-usual situation, and drive social, environmental, and economic progress.

However, these innovative business models and financial mechanisms require a supportive ecosystem to thrive. This includes access to low-cost financing, regulatory support, and market conditions that reward sustainable practices. Collaboration between businesses, financial institutions, and governments is essential to create this ecosystem and scale the deployment of innovative solutions.

Developing innovative business models and financial mechanisms is not just about mitigating climate change but also about unlocking new opportunities for economic growth and development. By embracing innovation, businesses and investors can drive the net-zero transition while creating value for shareholders, customers, and society.

4. The Financial Sector's Role in Green Capital Mobilization and Climate Risk Management

The financial sector plays a pivotal role in the net-zero transition by mobilizing green capital and managing climate-related financial risks. However, this requires a fundamental shift in how financial institutions assess risk, allocate capital, and engage with clients and stakeholders.

Investors could redefine their investment strategies to meet specific carbon emission reduction targets corresponding to a certain timeline, including re-developing their policy statement, demonstrating commitment through appropriate disclosures, and redefining the fund managers' role and mandate. Other steps include conducting strategic portfolio allocation to reduce carbon emissions over time, reallocating the portfolio if it is not meeting carbon-emission targets, and advising clients on climate risk and opportunity. Institutional investors can also engage with policymakers and regulators to create appropriate financial policies and regulations for the sector's overall development concerning climate change. Institutional investors can act as environmental stewards and actively engage with corporates through proxy voting or board representation to push climate change agenda in business decision-making.

Banks can realign their lending portfolio with a carbon emission reduction target corresponding to a certain timeline and deploy lending strategies accordingly. This strategy will require banks to lower financing to heavy carbon-emitting businesses over time and increase their lending portfolio to alternative low or no-carbon emission sectors. Banks should differentiate clients based on their contribution to climate change and risk, thereby easing the identification of low-emission lendees. In addition, banks can also finance corporations' negative emission technologies and projects.

Financial Services Providers, including credit rating agencies, investment banks, and brokerage houses, are important in reducing carbon emissions generated through the financial system. Credit ratings act as an indicator and play a crucial role in loan and bond financing; they must incorporate climate change to improve the robustness of the rating model and send the right signal to investors on the impact of climate change risk on debt financing. Similarly, brokerage houses should spread awareness of climate risk and opportunities among retail and institutional investors, making the financial market responsive to this imminent risk.

Moreover, the financial sector must deploy new financial products and services that support the mobilization of green capital. This includes green bonds, sustainability-linked loans, and climate transition funds that finance projects and companies contributing to the net-zero transition. These financial instruments are designed to meet the needs of a diverse class of investors. Some investors want to improve their returns by shuffling their portfolios favouring sustainable businesses, while others aim to mitigate sustainability and climate change risk.

Financial institutions must integrate climate risk into their core decision-making processes to support the net-zero transition. This includes assessing the physical and transition risks associated with climate change and incorporating them into their lending, investment, and underwriting practices. By doing so, financial institutions can ensure that their portfolios are aligned with the goals of the Paris Agreement and are resilient to the impacts of climate change.

Engagement and stewardship are also critical components of the financial sector's role in the net-zero transition. By engaging with companies on climate strategies and voting on shareholder resolutions, investors can influence corporate behaviour and encourage companies to adopt more ambitious climate targets. Institutional investors' active engagement can include managing risks concerning climate change and disclosing their engagement reports with the investee companies. Stewardship activities can also help to improve transparency and accountability, ensuring that companies are making meaningful progress toward their climate goals.

5. The Role of Financial Regulators to Accelerate Green Financing and Mitigating Climate-Related Financial Risks

Regulators can also promote the integration of climate change into financial decision-making. By encouraging the adoption of climate finance frameworks and standards, regulators can ensure that banks and financial institutions take a holistic approach to risk management and consider the long-term impacts of their investments and lending practices. Furthermore, financial regulators can play a role in fostering innovation in green finance by providing guidance and support for developing new financial products and services. This includes working with industry stakeholders to establish standards and best practices for green bonds, sustainability-linked loans, and other financial instruments that support the net-zero transition.

Policy Area	*Policy*	*Instruments*
Financial Policy and Regulatory Tools	Transparency of climate risks	Development of a repository of climate-related financial data, disclosure, scenario analysis, and stress testing
	Governance	Incorporation of climate change risk in supervisory practices
	Accelerating green finance through regulation	Differential capital requirements based on the green intensity of assets
	Supporting the development of green financial securities	Guidelines/taxonomy for green finance instruments, low-carbon indices, and platforms
Monetary Policy Tools	Encourage green financing through selective credit control.	RBI can increase the Cash Reserve Ratio (CRR) and Statutory Lending Ratio (SLR) requirements for carbon-intensive projects to decrease high-carbon lending capacity while reducing the reserve ratio for green investments, thereby increasing credit flows towards green projects. RBI can determine the repo rate, reverse repo, and bank rate based on the financed emission intensity of regulated entities. RBI can reduce the margin money requirements of green projects while increasing the same for carbon-intensive projects.
	Moral Suasion	RBI can nudge commercial banks to accelerate capital flows toward green sectors while striving to mitigate climate-related financial risk RBI can spread awareness of climate-related risks while encouraging capital flows towards green projects.

The Reserve Bank of India (RBI) can incentivize banks to drive credit to green projects with lower risk weightage for extending credit to green loans and green bonds. The central bank can consider green as a priority sector for lending, making it mandatory for banks to allocate a minimum percentage of lending to the green industries and offer better credit terms to green companies/projects. RBI can also consider green lending as collateral for refinancing.

The bond and equity market can mobilize household savings through insurance and pension funds for sustainable businesses while ensuring compliance with their investment regulations. Pension funds and insurance companies have long investment horizons, which pairs well with the needs of several low-carbon businesses that require long-term capital. Pension Fund Regulatory Development Authority (PFRDA) and Insurance Regulatory Development Authority (IRDA) can make investing in Green Securities and other green/sustainable activities desirable for pension and insurance funds. These regulators can set a minimum portfolio asset allocation by insurance and pension funds to the green sector as their long-duration liability will be more prone to climate change risk.

Financial regulators have a critical role in ensuring that the economic system is resilient to the risks posed by climate change. As climate-related risks become increasingly material, regulators must take proactive measures to mitigate these risks and ensure the stability of the financial system. A growing number of central banks and financial regulators have warned that climate and environmental risks could fundamentally affect their core mandate - maintaining economic stability. Financial regulators should suggest India-specific guidelines for adoption on integrating climate risks and stress testing (focusing on physical climate resilience).

One of the key responsibilities of financial regulators is to develop and enforce climate-related disclosure requirements. By requiring financial institutions and companies to disclose their exposure to climate risks and strategies for managing them, regulators can improve transparency and enable investors to make informed decisions. Disclosure requirements also incentivize companies to adopt more sustainable practices, as their stakeholders hold them accountable.

In addition to disclosure requirements, regulators can conduct scenario analysis and climate stress tests to assess the resilience of financial institutions to climate-related risks. These tests can help to identify vulnerabilities in the economic system and inform the development of policies and regulations that enhance the system's resilience.

Besides, RBI may direct banks to incorporate climate change risk in lending practices and regularly assess the impact of climate change risk impact on its portfolio exposure. Central Bank should consider embedding climate risk assessment into the supervisory review to create transparency for banks and FIs regarding the supervisors' approach towards climate-related and environmental risks.

The Insurance Regulatory and Development Authority (IRDA) and Pension Fund Regulatory and Development Authority (PFRDA) can direct insurance and pension fund management companies, respectively, to assess their portfolio against climate change risk and rebalance their portfolio if necessary. Securities and Exchange Board of India (SEBI) can direct mutual funds to consider climate change risk assessment of the portfolio as a fiduciary responsibility.

The role of financial regulators in the net-zero transition is multifaceted. By improving transparency, enhancing risk management, and fostering innovation, regulators can contribute to the resilience and sustainability of the financial system, ensuring that it supports global efforts to mitigate climate change.

6. Support from Developed Countries for Developing Countries' Green Transition

The global nature of climate change requires a collaborative approach that includes support from developed countries for the green transition in developing nations. Developing countries, which are often more vulnerable to the impacts of climate change, require financial, technical, and capacity-building support to pursue low-carbon development pathways.

Developed countries are responsible for fulfilling their climate finance commitments made under international agreements, such as the Paris Agreement. This includes providing grants, concessional loans, and other financial assistance to help developing countries invest in low-carbon technologies and build climate-resilient infrastructure.

In addition to financial support, developed countries can also facilitate technology transfer and capacity building. This includes sharing knowledge and expertise on low-carbon technologies, supporting research and development in developing countries, and providing training and education to build local capacity.

Developed countries have pledged to assist developing countries with USD 100 billion annually in combating climate mitigation and adaptation. The Government of India has, on several occasions, stressed that the developed countries must fulfill their climate finance obligations. India has emphasized that international public climate finance must be beyond developmental or aid funding. The existing climate finance in terms of loans, guarantees, and export credits from development banks to developing countries cannot be considered international climate finance. The developed world must step up and ensure that investment shortfall in developing countries, including India, is fulfilled through international climate finance commitments.

7. Multilateral Development Banks: Change in Capital Deployment Strategy

Since the gap between capital needs and expected mobilization is huge, there will be an investment shortfall in developing countries' (including India) climate action plans even if all the necessary steps are taken. In this context, the role of MDBs will be crucial to bridge the expected investment shortfall.

International climate finance mostly provides loans and, lately, equity developmental projects, including climate-friendly projects in developing countries, rather than credit enhancement instruments such as guarantees or subordinate debt, which have a greater ability to crowd in private capital. The heavy reliance on loans does not help developing countries attract private capital. MDBs should change their capital deployment strategy and use risk-mitigating financial instruments such as guarantees, insurance, and local currency hedging, which can de-risk project/business or financial risk. These mitigating risk instruments can bridge projects and private capital, thereby crowding in the much-needed private capital to green projects.

In principle, additionality and leverage should be the two principles of the MDB capital deployment strategy. Since MDBs are funded by Sovereign Governments, additionally created by MDBs is an important criterion. In the case of green projects, additionality is more critical for MDBs as these projects mitigate carbon emissions, which is a global problem, and can address free rider concerns. Leverage is essential since the total amount of MDBs is too low to meet all the development projects.

DFIs and MDBs can provide critical capital, manage risks, share knowledge, and develop institutional capacity and partnerships for development projects in the target countries. MDBs and DFIs can support vulnerable countries by strengthening administrative and financial structures for better transparency and accountability, which can help these vulnerable countries access global public capital. They can support the countries in identifying and designing projects to develop pipeline projects for funding.